MAGNETIC-BUBBLE MEMORY TECHNOLOGY

ELECTRICAL ENGINEERING AND ELECTRONICS

A Series of Reference Books and Textbooks

Editors

Marlin O. Thurston
Department of Electrical
Engineering
The Ohio State University
Columbus, Ohio

William Middendorf
Department of Electrical
and Computer Engineering
University of Cincinnati
Cincinnati, Ohio

Electronics Editor

Marvin H. White
Westinghouse Electric Corporation
Defense and Space Center
Baltimore, Maryland

1. Rational Fault Analysis, *edited by Richard Saeks and S. R. Liberty*

2. Nonparametric Methods in Communications,
   edited by P. Papantoni-Kazakos and Dimitri Kazakos

3. Interactive Pattern Recognition, *Yi-tzuu Chien*

4. Solid-State Electronics, *Lawrence E. Murr*

5. Electronic, Magnetic, and Thermal Properties of Solid Materials,
   Klaus Schröder

6. Magnetic-Bubble Memory Technology, *Hsu Chang*

Other Volumes in Preparation

MAGNETIC-BUBBLE MEMORY TECHNOLOGY

Hsu Chang

IBM Corporation
Thomas J. Watson Research Center
Yorktown Heights, New York

MARCEL DEKKER, INC.   New York and Basel

528737201

Library of Congress Cataloging in Publication Data

Chang, Hsu [Date]
    Magnetic-bubble memory technology.

    (Electrical engineering and electronics; v. 6)
    Includes bibliographical references and index.
    1. Magnetic memory (Calculating-machines) 2. Magnetic
bubble devices. I. Title. II. Series.
TK7895.M3C43   621.3819'58'33   78-15007
ISBN 0-8247-6795-0

This monograph was originally published as an article in
Encyclopedia of Computer Science and Technology, Volume 10.

MARCEL DEKKER, INC.
270 Madison Avenue, New York, New York 10016

Current printing (last digit):
10 9 8 7 6 5 4 3 2 1

PRINTED IN THE UNITED STATES OF AMERICA

To my parents
Shen-fu and Shu-hwa Fan Chang
on their seventieth birthdays

PREFACE

Available books on bubbles were prepared and published before the appearance of real products in 1977 (e. g., Texas Instruments' 92 kb memory modules and portable electronic data terminals, and Western Electric's voice recorders). They extensively covered the basic materials and physics, as well as device concepts and experimental studies, but failed to cover bubble products. However, the products are the tangible realization of technological aspirations, and the fruitful consolidation of diverse disciplines. Therefore, we devote this book to the description of current bubble products and the projection of future applications.

This manuscript was originally prepared as a chapter for the Marcel Dekker Encyclopedia of Computer Science and Technology. Put in that context instead of the field of magnetics, the focus was naturally placed on applications. While the current applications are revealed in current products, the future applications must be speculated and assessed in terms of technology extendability and system implications. Thus we discuss the following topics in the book:

Current technology status and products

Versatility of shift registers and major/minor loops (with a view to stretch the
        life of current products)

Forecast for LSI bubbles (an assessment of the potentials and problems in
        improving bubble chip density and capacity)

Subsystems, architectures, and programming; performance (a collection of
        current thinking, to pave the way for evaluation and innovation)

The majority of the references cited were published after 1975. Indeed, after the breakthroughs in materials and devices in earlier years, progress towards products has been made only in recent years. It is anticipated that the availability of basic components will further extend applications and spur system innovations. Given the dramatic cost reduction anticipated and the versatility of bubble devices, significant advances are expected in the system areas which are ill-defined at present but are bound to flourish in the future.

The author is indebted to many colleagues, both inside and outside of IBM, whose works are quoted extensively in the text. However, any faults in the structure and emphasis of the book are the author's own responsiblity. He is also grateful to Betty Smalley, who typed the manuscript in the evenings after her busy day schedule.

Hsu Chang

CONTENTS

MAGNETIC-BUBBLE MEMORY TECHNOLOGY

INTRODUCTION

General Background

The official date of conception of bubble technology was March 22, 1966, when Bell Laboratories engineers and scientists Bobeck, Gianola, Hagedorn, Scovil, Shockley, and their co-workers assembled to search for storage media better than Permalloy for use in waffle-iron memory structures [1]. The outcome was new storage materials with anisotropy (easy direction of magnetization) normal to the medium plane, and the replacement of the waffle-iron structure by planar, and hence more configurable, overlays. These mutations paved the way for the integrated-circuit fabrication of bubble devices—the first LSI (large-scale integration) magnetic device.

The technology made its debut in the business world on August 8, 1969, when both the Wall Street Journal and New York Times reported the issuance of U.S. Patent 3,460,116 which described Magnetic Domain Propagation Circuit invented by A. H. Bobeck, U. F. Gianola, R. C. Sherwood, and W. Shockley. The news items heralded bubble devices as a contender for electronic files to replace mechanical disk files.

Nearly a decade later, several products have been announced. They started with Hitachi's (Japan) 32 kbyte unit (18 chips each of 16×10^3 bits, 0.1 MHz data rate, and 160 msec to read out 16×10^3 bits), which was priced at $667 in October 1975. Rockwell International (U.S.A.) and Plessey (England) announced similar products shortly after. However, more viable "product" configurations are probably Texas Instruments tiny memory modules (10^5 bits) [Electronics, p. 40, March 17, 1977], and NASA/Rockwell's bubble recorder (10^8 bits) [Electronics, p. 31, January 6, 1977]. The TI module is a 25 g, $1.1 \times 1 \times 0.4$ in.^{3}, 0.5 W, 14 pin, dual-in-line self-contained package of 92 kbits.

1

The package(s) can serve as a storage unit for and share a circuit board with a microprocessor. It takes up only a small fraction of the space, consumes far less power, requires much simpler interface electronics, and provides much higher speed than a mechanical storage unit. The implications for terminals and office equipment are highly significant.

NASA/Rockwell is readying for use in space during 1978 a 10^8 bit bubble recorder which consists of 64 memory cells, with each cell of 1.6×10^6 bits in a $3 \times 1.5 \times 0.5$ in.^{3} volume. The complete recorder will occupy 600 in.^{3}, weigh 40 lb, and require 100 W power (maximum). It offers a 1.2 MHz data rate, 0.5 sec access time, and a reliability of 4×10^4 hr mean-time-between-failures. This recorder will be the first electronic file which offers storage capacity comparable to present-day disk or drum fixed-head files.

Even though bubble technology has entered into the marketplace, debates on its future have not abated. For compact modular storages required in terminals and office data-processing equipments, bubbles compete with CCD's and floppy disks. For backing stores used in storage hierarchies, bubbles compete with CCD's and fixed-head disk files. For large-capacity secondary storages in the future, bubbles will compete with moving-head disk files and electronic beam addressable memories. The competition is reflected in both technical conferences and business journals. For instance, the 1977 Spring CompCon featured sessions on Mass Storage for Microprocessors and Mini-Micro Peripherals (bubbles vs minifloppy disks). While Texas Instruments ambitiously expects sales of bubble-memory components to exceed $100 million annually by 1979 (let us say 2×10^{11} bits at 0.05¢/bit) and half a billion dollars by 1985 (The bubble memory finally arrives, Business Week, March 28, 1977, pp. 72-74), the announcement of TI's first bubble product (a 92-kbit package) coincided with the announcement of its first CCD memory product (a 65-kbit chip) [Electronics, March 17, 1977, pp. 38-40].

The background sketched above suggests that while this article reviews the current status of bubbles, it should also address the questions:

What are the viable applications for bubbles?
Can bubbles compete with CCD's, disks, etc. in the long run by offering cost and
     performance advantages?

Bubble technology has been actively pursued by a wide spectrum of professionals ranging from solid-state physicists and materials scientists, to magnetics and electronics engineers, to packaging specialists and system designers. As of September 1977, about 1700 papers have been published and about 400 United States patents issued. This article concentrates on aspects related to applications. While technology information is often cited, physics and materials topics are kept to the minimum essentials. The following references are suggested for readers who intend to pursue beyond this article.

1. H. Chang, Magnetic Bubble Technology, IEEE Press/Wiley, New York, September 1975. A 200-page tutorial plus 46 reprint papers, reviewing genesis, devices, applications, physics, materials, and perspective. Also included are extensive bibliography and patent list up to 1975.
2. Annual Conference Proceedings of International Magnetics Conference (spring) and Magnetism and Magnetic Materials Conference (winter) (special issues published by IEEE Transactions on Magnetics and AIP Conference Proceedings, respectively).

BUBBLE BASICS

Bubble and Serpentine Domains

In suitably prepared magnetic materials, such as epitaxially grown magnetic garnet films, the easy directions of magnetization (micromagnets) are perpendicular to the film plane. In the absence of external fields, the film plane is divided into two regions of intertwined serpentines, one with upward magnetization, the other with downward magnetization, so as to achieve a minimum-energy magnetostatic equilibrium (see Fig. 1a). As a bias field is applied normal to the film plane, the region with magnetization parallel to the field will grow at the expense of the other region (see Figs. 1b to 1h). Eventually, the serpentines in the region with magnetization opposite to the field will shrink to circular cylindrical domains (nicknamed magnetic bubbles due to their resemblance to highly mobile bubbles on water surface). Further increase of magnetic bias field will collapse the bubbles. However, decreasing the bias field will restore the serpentine domains (Figs. 1i to 1ℓ).

The formation of bubbles and serpentine domains can be analyzed on the basis of the energy minimization principle. The relevant energy terms include anisotropy energy (responsible for easy direction of magnetization), magnetostatic energy (responsible for domains with opposite magnetization directions), exchange energy (responsible for allowing only gradual rather than step-like change in magnetization directions), and applied field energy (responsible for orienting magnetization in the field direction). Kooy and Enz [2] were the first to report the phenomena, and Bobeck [3] pioneered in their application to bubble devices.

The bubble and serpentine domain phenomena can be quantitatively summarized in Fig. 2. There are several features noteworthy for device applications.

1. Stable bubbles exist over a range of bias field (stable storage).
2. A bubble can be elongated by lowering the bias field for further manipulation

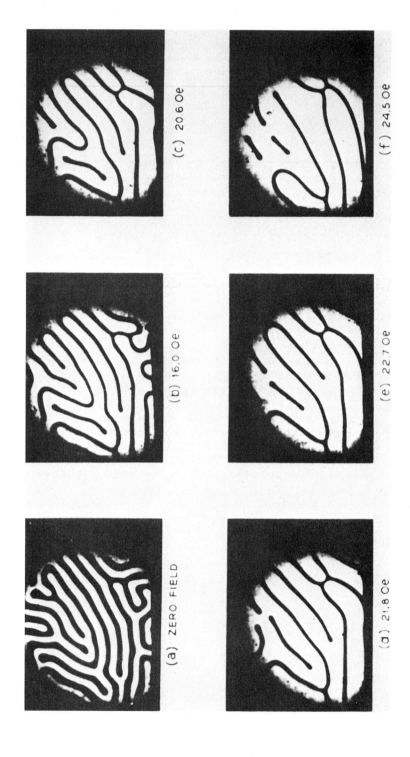

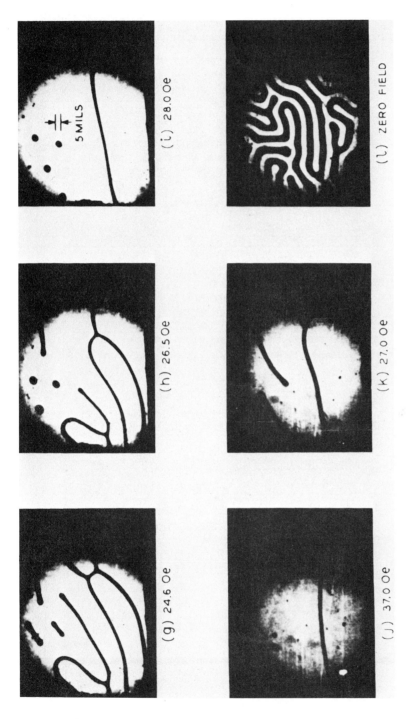

FIG. 1. Bubble and serpentine domain configurations as a function of bias field. Pictures are obtained by the Faraday magnetooptic effect in a 2.3-mil thick $TmFeO_3$ platelet. Sample originally demagnetized (a). Field applied normal to the surface, first increased, then decreased. Note at (g) that the strip in the upper left-hand corner became a cylindrical domain. This, and the other cylindrical domains which formed, reduced in size until (j), when three of five collapsed. As the field is decreased the remaining two bubbles open into strips (k) and eventually grow to fill the entire platelet (l). (After Bobeck [3], Fig. 17.)

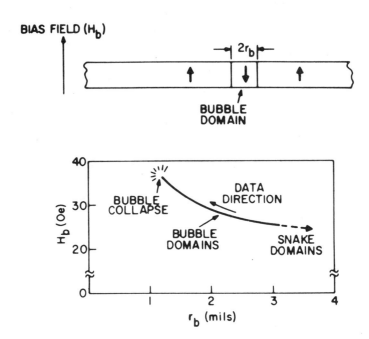

FIG. 2. Cylindrical domain radius (r) as a function of an applied bias field (H_b) in a 2.3-mil thick $TmFeO_3$ platelet. (After Bobeck [3], Fig. 16.)

(for example, replication for generation of new bubbles or nondestructive readout).

3. A bubble can be annihilated by raising the bias field (storage clearance).

4. Not revealed by Fig. 2, however, it is known that the nucleation field is much higher than the wall motion field (hence bubble movement without spurious bubble generation).

Basic Functions for a Memory

Before we discuss practical device structures, let us review how the bubble phenomena can be translated into basic functions for memory devices.

Storage. ONE and ZERO can be represented by the presence or absence of a bubble at a given bit location.

Propagation, Access, and Memory Organization. Bubbles (conceived as tiny magnets) can be attracted and/or repelled into motion by other moving magnets. The "other moving magnets" can be provided by field-activated Permalloy patterns or current-activated conductor loops. The arrangement of Permalloy patterns or conductor loops determines the access method and memory organization.

Read and Detection. To provide a means for read, we must invoke an additional phenomenon—magnetoresistive effect. A strip of Permalloy will change its resistance by a few percent in the presence of an external field such as is provided by a bubble passing by.

Clear. An information bit is cleared when a bubble representing it is annihilated or discarded.

Write. An information bit is written when a bubble is created (by nucleation or replication) to represent it.

Major/Minor Loop Chip Organization

Consider Fig. 3 as a typical example of a bubble memory chip. This example is chosen since it is from one of the first bubble memory products (Texas Instruments' TBM0103, see Ref. 4). Several other companies are also manufacturing or developing similar chips. Moreover, as we shall see below in the section entitled Versatility of Shift Registers and Major/Minor Loops, many improvements are in store to prolong and expand the usefulness of this type of chip.

The functions performed by various components in the chip can be better illustrated by the schematic in Fig. 4. Information is stored in many parallel closed-loop shift registers—called minor loops. Data will circulate in these loops normally. When read or write operation is to be performed, the access to the minor loops is provided by a common shift register (called major loop), which links not only all the minor loops but also a read circuit and a write circuit. Let us now describe the clear, write, and read operations. Since all bits in the chip are circulated in synchronization with the rotating field, the positions of all bits can be determined by clock timing the rotating field. A horizontal row of bits from corresponding positions in all minor loops (one per loop) can be considered as a word. A selected word can be moved to the TRANSFER gates adjacent to the major loop after a specific delay. All bits from the word can be transferred in parallel to the major loop, thus vacating their bit positions in the minor loops. The transferred word (bits in series), after a fixed delay (68 steps), will have its first bit at the REPLICATE gate. If destructive read (or clear) is intended, the REPLICATE gate will not be activated, and the bubbles will be passing through the DETECTOR and expelled from the array. On the other hand, if nondestructive read is intended, the bubbles will be replicated by the activated REPLICATE gate. While one bubble stream travels to the DETECTOR, the other will be returned to the TRANSFER gates. If the major loop and the minor loop are of "equal" length, the bits in the major loop when propagated to the TRANSFER gates will be re-aligned with the voids they left behind in the minor loops.

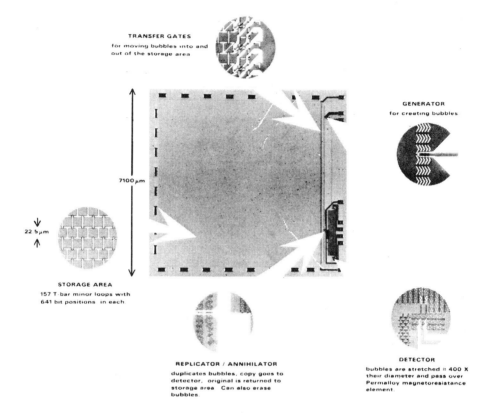

FIG. 3. Six functions of a bubble memory chip: storage, access (by propagation), selection (by transfer gates), NDRO or DRO (by replicator or annihilator), write (by generator), and read (by magnetoresistive detector). (After Juliussen [134], Fig. 1.)

Thus data can be restored into the minor loops. If new information is to be written into the vacant positions, the GENERATE gate is to be activated to insert data into the cleared major loop, in proper time phase with the minor-loop vacancies. Again, the data are transferred from the major loop into the minor loops at the TRANSFER gates. In reality, since there are delays incurred in transfer-out and transfer-in, the TBM 0103 chip has the minor loop longer than the major loop by 1 bit to ensure that rewrite will restore the readout bits into their original bit positions.

Having demonstrated the read and write operations for the major/minor loop memory chip, we should take note of the very small number of interconnections for the entire chip (Fig. 4): two each for TRANSFER, GENERATION, and REPLI-CATION, and four for DETECTION, totaling ten for the chip. It is the high density devices and large number of bits on a chip, yet accessible by a small number of interconnections and offering complete functional capability right on the chip, which make the bubble devices an integrated circuit technology.

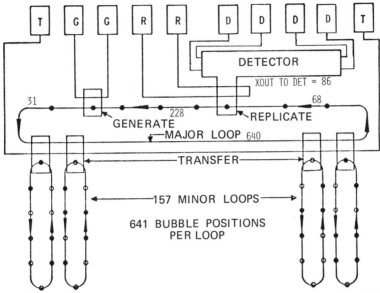

ELECTRONIC FUNCTIONS OBJECTIVE
MAGNETIC BUBBLE MEMORIES
100K BIT BUBBLE CHIP SCHEMATIC

FIG. 4. Schematic of a major/minor loop array (for Texas Instrument's bubble memory module TBM0103).

Components in a Major/Minor Loop Chip

We shall now describe the structures and operations of the chip components used for propagation, generation, replication, and detection (see Geusic [5]). An acquaintance with such components is essential in order to understand the chip operations, to assess the present and potential densities of bubble devices (see below in the sections entitled Current Technology Status, and Forecast for LSI Bubbles), and to evolve more advanced chip designs (see below in the sections entitled Versatility of Shift Registers and Major/Minor Loops, and Subsystems, Architectures, and Programming).

Refer to Fig. 5a. A propagation track consists of periodic structures of T-bar Permalloy patterns superimposed on a garnet storage medium. When a planar rotating field is applied, the long bars in the direction of the field are magnetized while those transverse to the field are much less affected. A bubble (or more precisely, the magnetic pole at the top end of a bubble) will be attracted by a pole of opposite polarity on a T-bar pattern. As the field rotates, the induced magnetic poles will appear at different locations of the T-bar patterns, thus shifting the bubbles along the propagation track. Figure 5a describes the motion in one cycle of clockwise field rotation.

Many comparable Permalloy overlay configurations have been evolved to provide the train of attractive poles to shift bubbles. Two of them are worth special mentioning. Figure 5b shows chevron patterns which provide multiple attractive poles to move a magnetic stripe (an elongated bubble). Since an increasing number of chevrons can be used in successive columns (see Fig. 5e), a bubble can be gradually elongated to achieve on-chip amplification. The elongation is in the

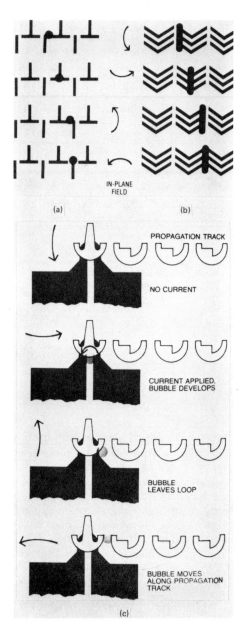

FIG. 5. Components in a major/minor loop chip. (a) T-bar propagation track. (b) Chevron propagation track. (c) Asymmetrical half-disk propagation track and a pick-axe/conductor nucleation-type bubble generator.

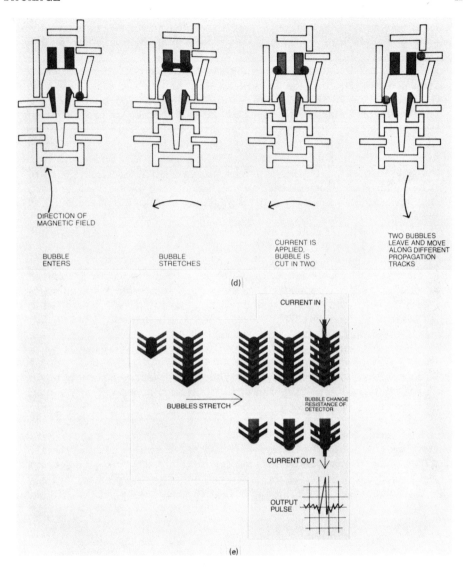

FIG. 5 (continued). (d) A fork structure for replicate/transfer (NDRO/DRO).
(e) A column of chevrons for stretch and detection. (After Geusic [5].)

direction transverse to propagation, and will not affect the propagation speed nor the data rate. Bobeck et al. [6] have reviewed the use of chevron patterns for logic, propagation, and transfer.

Another propagation structure (see Fig. 5c) is the asymmetrical half disk (see Bonyhard and Smith [7]). It is the most likely successor to T-bar devices in the present bubble products. The minimum feature in 16 μm-period T-bar devices is 1 μm. The minimum feature in 8 μm-period half-disk devices (improving density by a factor of 4) is also 1 μm. The minimum feature refers to an airgap between adjacent Permalloy patterns. The half disks have parallel tips between adjacent disks to bridge over a bubble. The thick side of the half disk provides a stronger attractive pole to facilitate bubble motion in the propagation direction, thus preventing the bubble from snapping back via the thinner side to the previous disk. Additional advantages include: (1) Only one discrete Permalloy feature and only one gap per propagate period, hence lower defects in processing; (2) fewer elements, hence large element per period; and (3) no Permalloy features shared between adjacent propagation tracks, hence reduced interaction between adjacent tracks. A complete chip design was presented by Bonyhard and Smith in their article [7].

A nucleation-type bubble generator to provide a means for write is depicted in Fig. 5c. A half disk is augmented with a center stem to provide at the disk edge a strong normal field to the storage medium when the rotating field is directed downward and parallel to the stem. When an aiding current is applied, a new bubble will be nucleated and propagated away in subsequent phases.

A replicate and transfer gate which permits nondestructive readout from the chip without re-write operation is shown in Fig. 5d. A bubble is moved onto a half disk. When it is stretched by the half disk in the next phase, a current is applied to cut the bubble in two. One half is propagated into the major loop track while the other is recirculated into the minor loop.

The detector (Fig. 5e) consists of two parts. One part is for stretching a bubble as discussed earlier. The other part, located at the end of the stretcher, consists of a Permalloy line zigzagging through the chevrons (to gain maximum length). As an elongated stripe propagates through the detector, it causes a resistance change in the zigzag magnetoresistive element, thus effecting a voltage change at its terminals. Signals of several millivolts have been achieved for bubbles with diameters smaller than 2 μm (i.e., density higher than 10^7 bits/in.^{2}).

Package

Similar to semiconductor devices, bubble chips can be mounted in dual-in-line packages (see Fig. 6). However, there are several different features. Permanent magnets are provided to supply the normal bias field. A pair of coils are provided to supply the planar rotating field. An initialize coil may be provided to create the first bubbles if replicate-type generators are used. The external housing provides a magnetic shield for the entire package.

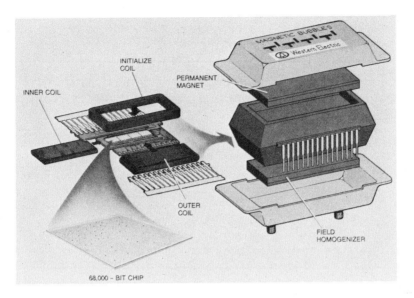

FIG. 6. Dual-in-line package for bubble memory devices. The package contains garnet chips, parts to create the perpendicular magnetic fields (permanent magnet and field homogenizer plus initialize coil), parts to create the in-plane rotating field (inner and outer coils), and the case for magnetic shielding. (After Geusic [5].)

CURRENT TECHNOLOGY STATUS

We shall present the current status by first introducing the commercial interests in bubble technology, followed by summaries of chip characteristics, chip fabrication, packaging, and testing.

Commercial Interests

Domestic and foreign companies in active commercial pursuit of the bubble technology are presented in Table 1.

Bell Systems, where the first bubble devices were invented, has explored bubble applications in repertory dialers (2000 bit capacity to store 10 telephone numbers for immediate recall), voice message recording (2.7×10^5 bits to record 12 sec of digitized voice message, see below in the section entitled Western Electric's Announcement System and Serial Bubble Store), and fixed-head-file replacement (10^8 bits for telephone exchange centers). It is of interest to note that in addition to storage, the repertory dialer features bubble implementation of direct decimal coding of numbers, counters, and control circuits [8]. Many bubble patents on switching network applications have been issued [9, pp. 117-122]. It is surmised that when bubbles do replace fixed-head files, it will not be a one-for-one storage replacement, but an upgrading to storage with processing capabilities.

Hewlett-Packard's interest in bubbles could be for hand-held and desk calculators, intelligent terminals, and instruments for signal display, processing, and

TABLE 1
Commercial Interests of Various Companies

Bell	Repertory dialers Voice recording Telephone exchange
Fujitsu	Terminals Drum replacement Electronic switching systems
HP	Calculators Terminals Instruments
Hitachi	Office machines Point of sale machines Character display Electronic switching system
IBM	Disk replacements (floppy, fixed, and moving heads)
NEC	Intelligent terminal Program loader Chinese character generator
NTT	Electronic switching systems
Plessey	Telecommunication and military applications View data teletext Disk and cassette replacement New applications (bubbles + microprocessors)
Rockwell	Flight tape recorder replacement (NASA) Block organized store
TI	Portable data terminal Disk replacement

generation. At present, the 9800 series desk-top calculators have only several thousand bytes of read-write memory to accommodate a few thousand programming steps (e.g., 9815A has a 3000-byte read-write memory for 2008 program steps). The shirt-pocket programmable calculators only offer a few hundred programming steps. It is known that a good programmer can manage 10^6 byte storage on her/his own.

Hitachi is the first company to announce a bubble product (Electronic News, October 20, 1975). The 18-chip 32-kbyte unit is intended for storage unit in office machines, point-of-sale machines, and character displays.

IBM, being a major innovator and manufacturer of magnetic disk products, is greatly interested in bubbles as a challenger to and possible replacement for disks. Its research effort appears to have more emphasis on high density (e.g., bubble lattice files and contiguous disks, see below in the section entitled Device Concept Improvement) and low-cost media (e.g., amorphous films) with an aspiration for moving-head-disk-file replacement.

NASA has been sponsoring research and development work on bubbles (mainly at Rockwell) since 1969. Its main interest is a 10^8-bit storage module of 10^5-bit shift register chips for flight tape recorder replacement. Qualified modules are being readied for flight test in 1978. (See below in the section entitled Rockwell's Solid-State Data Recorder and POS-8.) Plans for 10^9-bit bubble recorder are also under consideration. (See below in the section entitled Current Government Programs.) The technology competence at Rockwell has also led to its interest in commercial applications. In 1976 a product POS-8 was announced. The system characteristics are: 0.8×10^6 bits (8 10^5-bit shift registers on 8 chips), 800 kHz bit rate (8 in parallel), 0.5 sec average access time, 2.5 lb weight, 12.8 W power consumption, 50 in.^{3} volume, 9720 hr MTBF, 10^{-12} soft error/read, and 10^{-13} hard error/read. The system is capable of nonvolatile storage, nondestructive readout, start and stop operation, and 0 to 50°C operation. According to the sales brochure, possible applications include "intelligent terminals, multiple-purpose displays, super calculators, micro-computer peripherals, back-up for volatile main memories, data records, point-of-sale systems, data entry, store and forward, numerical control, industrial control, credit authorization, text editing and secretarial service functions."

Nippon Telephone and Telegraphy has announced the use of bubbles for its electronic switching systems. The major advantages (see Tsuboya et al. [10]) of bubbles in such applications are maintenance-free, easy-transportation, small volume, and high reliability (read error rate $< 9 \times 10^{-12}$/read). It is estimated that the annual volume requirement is 5×10^{11} bits.

Plessy expects bubble memories to find a place in hierarchical computer-memory systems with a capacity of 0.5 to 10 Mbits. As FHF replacement, bubbles will be used for paging and buffer memories. They will also become competitive with floppy disks and tape cassettes in applications with no removability requirements (e.g., data collection, point-of-sales, stock control). New applications, especially in conjunction with microprocessors, will also be emphasized (Data Processing 18(5), 36 (July/August 1976)).

Texas Instruments [11] introduced a 92-kbit bubble memory module and bubble portable data terminals into the market in 1977 (see below in the section entitled Texas Instrument's Bubble Memory Modules and Portable Data Terminals). Hand-held, programmable calculators could be turned into powerful minicomputers (almost) by adding bubble memories. Other bubble applications are expected in word processing systems, home computers, microprocessors, and minicomputers. TI is also building 128-kbit bubble chips into 2×10^6-bit modules that will have a data input/output rate of 2 MHz [11]. From these modules TI will construct prototypes of a 16×10^6-bit electronic drum system and two 10^8-bit recorder systems.

Three new contenders in the bubble memory market are Signetics (jointly with Philips), National, and Intel. It is noteworthy that these companies used to be dedicated to making semiconductor memories only (see Electronics 5(4), 75-76 (February 16, 1978)).

Technology Status

The essential features of bubble technology will be described in terms of chip characteristics, chip fabrication, packaging, and testing.

Table 2 is a summary of essential chip characteristics. The bit density is determined by bubble size, since bubbles must be spaced apart by about 4 diameters' distance to avoid adjacent bit interaction. Hence the bit size is 16d^2 where d = bubble diameter for discrete-bubble devices (e.g., T-bar, half disks) regardless of the

TABLE 2
Chip Characterization

	BTL	TI	Fujitsu
Bubble material	YSmLu–CaGe	YSmLu–CaGe	YEuYb–CaGe
Stripe width (μm)	3.4	5.4	3.1
Circuit period (μm)	16	22.5	14
Minimum feature (μm)	2	1.25	1
Alignment (μm)	±1	±0.5	
Chip capacity (kbit)	68	100	80
Chip size (mil^2)	238 × 205	365 × 335	208 × 168
Chips/package	4	1	4
Drive field (Oe)	40	40	40
Bias field margin (Oe)	14	8 to 16	
Frequency (kHz)	350	250	500
Power (W) chip	0.277		
Power (W) coil	1.588	0.5	
Temperature (°C)	30 to 80	25 to 75	
Detection	Every other bit		
Error rate (1/bubble/step)	$< 10^{-13}$		
Redundancy	None		PROM
Start/stop	By block		
References	7, 8, 135	15, 136	84

Permalloy overlay design. The bubble material is first of all chosen to provide
small bubble size (about equal to stripe width), and then to provide high speed and
large operating margin (i.e., large margin over wide temperature range). The
dependence of bubble size on physical properties and, in turn, their dependence on
the choice of materials were detailed in many papers and reviewed in Chapter V of
Chang's book [9]. A more recent review of bubble domain memory materials was
presented by Nielsen [13].

Current bubble devices (14 to 25 μm circuit period, or 1 to 2×10^6 bit/in.^{2}
device density) are already imposing very stringent requirements on photolithography and in fact almost approaching its fundamental limitations. Even though the
circuit period is determined by the bubble diameter, much could be done in Permalloy overlay design so as to relax the lithography requirements (i.e., minimum
feature and alignment). The T-bar devices (e.g., see TI column of Table 2) have
a width of the Permalloy patterns equal to 0.5d and a gap between T and bar (the
minimum feature) equal to 0.2d. The half-disk device of more recent vintage (e.g.,
see BTL column) has the gap between adjacent elements equal to 0.5d. Thus, given
1 μm as the photolithography limit, T-bar devices as optimized by Fujitsu have
already reached the limit (1 μm minimum feature, 3.1 μm bubble diameter, 1.5 ×
10^6 bit/in.^{2} density). By contrast, the half-disk devices can be further scaled down
to achieve 4 time density improvement (1 μm minimum feature, 1.7 μm bubble

diameter, 6×10^6 bit/in.^{2} density). More dramatic approaches to achieve even higher density will be discussed below in the section entitled Forecast for LSI Bubbles.

Bit density and chip capacity measure the degrees of integration. The TI modules contain 100 kbits per chip. Rockwell is pursuing a 1-μm bubble 10^6-bit chip [14]. In order to share the package and electronics cost, the trend is toward multiple chips per package. It is essential that the characteristics of the chips are sufficiently close in order to share the same bias and drive fields provided by the package. On the other hand, in order to reduce power dissipation, multiple packages are desirable since inactive chips need not be driven.

The data rate of the bubble memory minor loops is equal to the frequency of the drive field. Due to spatial constraint, the bits transferred from the minor loops only fill up every other position in the major loop. Moreover, the elongated domains in the chevron-column expander are prevented from interacting only when they occupy every other bit position. Thus the data rate of a major loop is only one-half the drive-field frequency. The data from several chips could be connected in parallel, thus yielding a much higher memory-module data throughput.

The power dissipation is mostly in the drive coils. At present it averages to 5 μW per bit at 100 kHz frequency and 30 μW at 350 kHz.

Chip Fabrication

The typical Permalloy field-access magnetic bubble devices are conductor first, two-level circuits deposited on top of magnetic garnet storage films. The fabrication steps are summarized below (for example, see Bullock et al. [15]):

Ion-implanted epitaxial garnet film (storage medium with hard bubble suppression)
RF plasma deposited 1000 Å SiO_2 (stress buffer and isolation layer)
Evaporated (at 200°C) 4500 Å Al-Cu; ion-milled patterns with tapered edges (low stress, electromigration-resistant conductors to control bubble generation, transfer, replication, and annihilation)
RF plasma deposited 10,000 Å SiO_2
RF sputtered (at 350°C) 4500 Å Permalloy (81% Ni, 19% Fe target by weight); ion-milled patterns using a positive-resist process (low magnetostriction, low coercivity—0.8 to 1.2 Oe—high magnetoresistance, $\Delta\rho/\rho \sim 3\%$)
RF plasma deposited 5000 Å SiO_2 (passivation)
Plasma etching (pad openings to Permalloy and Al-Cu levels)
Deposition of Au-Cr (bonding pads to Al-Cu and Permalloy pads)
Ultrasonic bonding to 1 mil Au wire

The process is monitored by several means. Coercivity and anisotropy are measured on bulk Permalloy disks. An array of Permalloy bars is monitored. The absence of B-H loop hysteresis is a viable sign that ion-milling has done no damage to the bar edges. Quasistatic propagation in-plane drive field is another monitoring parameter. The effect of Permalloy step over the conductor is monitored both by the bubble collapse field (acceptable if increase less than 1 Oe), and nucleation field along a < 110 > direction in the (111) plane (acceptable if increase less than 3.2%).

Advances toward chips of 2 μm bubble diameter (from the present 5 μm) and 10^6-bit capacity (from the present 10^5 bits) are based on new device designs (gap-tolerant half-disks or asymmetrical chevrons) and improved processing. Chrome masks fabricated by electron-beam techniques and 1 μm minimum-feature contact photolithography will be used (see Fontana et al. [16]). A lower plasma etching rate of SiO_2 is found to cause less degradation of bias field margin (see Stein et al. [17]).

An improved processing to produce planar structure has been demonstrated by Rose [18]. The process enables a thicker conductor metalization (8000 Å) than conventional processing, without the ill effects of the Permalloy step. The thicker conductors provide superior wire-bonding capability, lower line resistance, and longer electromigration failure lifetime.

The planar process is attained by anodizing a thick aluminum alloy film in all regions where no conductor is needed. When an Al film is anodized, the resulting oxide is thicker than the original Al film by as much as 60%. This must be compensated for by removing 30% of the portion of Al-Cu which will be oxidized. The Al-Cu layer, including the anodized portion, provides a flat underlayer for further deposition and delineation of Permalloy patterns.

Packaging

The mechanical configuration of a bubble memory package was described briefly above in Fig. 6. Also see below in the section entitled Rockwell's Solid State Data Recorder and POS-8 (Fig. 13). The module fabrication [19] can be divided into those operations dealing with the bubble memory chip itself (dicing, bonding, etc.) and operations related to the magnetics (coils and magnet structure). The assembly steps connected with the chip itself easily lend themselves to high volume semiconductor processing. On the other hand, production techniques had to be established for building perfect layered free-standing coils, assembling magnetic structures, magnetizing these structures to the proper bias level, and combining all these components into one device. Implementing these various techniques has been supported by a number of mature industries such as the coil-winding industry, the permanent magnet industry, and the magnetic-shielding industry. Moreover, before introducing the new packages into the marketplace, extensive environmental testing must be conducted which includes temperature cycle, thermal shock, mechanical shock, high temperature at high humidity, and high temperature life test.

The in-plane drive field can be supplied by several geometries of coils: orthogonal concentric rectangular solenoids [20], reflection coils [21], and folded-inner coil [22]. The first is most efficient in volume utilization, while the other two offer convenience in assembly. The coils are intended to produce planar fields to move bubbles in the chips, but unavoidably produce normal fields which affect bubble operating margins. Judd et al. [23] have calculated the various field components in multilayered rectangular solenoids. The effects of nearby magnetic materials within the bubble package are also included. The analysis facilitates the study of manufacturing variations, such as unequal turns per layer and coil or bubble chip misalignment, on the magnitude and uniformity of the rotating field. The results have been applied in aiding the design of the package in a digital voice storage application [24].

The data rate in a bubble chip is limited by the bubble mobility (a storage medium property) as well as by power dissipation in drive coils (due to eddy currents). The coil heating can quickly increase the chip temperature beyond allowable limits at high frequency. For example, a drive coil for 2 Mbits dissipates 5 W at 100 kHz, but 22 W at 500 kHz, raising the chip temperature by 55 °K. Saito et al. [25]

have designed and produced coils using litz wires (i.e., thin enameled wires bundled and stranded) to reduce eddy-current loss. A 2-Mbit module can be operated at 40 Oe in a rotating field of 500 kHz, with only 8 W coil loss.

Carlo et al. [26] discuss multichip package vs single-chip package, based on considerations of system volume, system power, and available drive transistors.

In bubble packages the bias field H_b is supplied by a Ba-ferrite permanent magnet structure. The magnitude of H_b may be appreciably altered after setting due to transient exposure to an externally applied magnetic field H_{ext} as much as 10 times smaller than the field used in setting H_b. DeBonte and Zappulla [27] examine this effect for a particular magnet design having a Permalloy yoke, a gap of 0.27 in., and a saturation field H_{sat} of 240 Oe. They find that setting by demagnetizing from saturation yields superior stability to setting by magnetizing from the demagnetized state, and stability of the set magnet may be further improved by demagnetizing with an alternating field.

In order for the bubble package to operate over a wide temperature range, it is necessary to provide a bias magnet system whose field strength as a function of temperature follows the bias margin range of the bubble chips. DeBonte and Butherus [28] have shown that the coefficient describing the linear variation of field strength with temperature for barium ferrite magnets is not a simple constant but depends on the permeance coefficient of the magnet geometrical structure.

The bubble memory module is housed in a magnetic shield. The preferred approach is to join (instead of welding) two pieces of preannealed magnetic shielding material by adhesives filled with high-permeability magnetic powders (resulting in adhesive permeability up to 10). De Bonte and Butherus [29] describe the formation and process for magnetically orienting the adhesive, and shield designs which are lighter, smaller, and provide more effective shielding.

The detailed mechanical structure and thermal package of a 256-kbit bubble memory module is given by Yu [30]. He then proceeds to characterize empirically the heat transfer problem in such a package. The two heat sources in such a package are the drive coils and the on-chip conductors. The maximum steady-state chip temperature rise over the magnet and the shield can be expressed in terms of the total chip power and the total coil power. Such information is important in ensuring temperature tracking between the chips and the bias magnets.

Testing

Bubble propagation on a magnetic circuit is not 100% reliable. Shumate et al. [31] have taken extensive mean-time-to-failure data and studied their dependence on temperature, circuit design, ion-implantation dosage, circuit defects, and operating frequency.

The testing of bubble-device wafers, chips, and assembled packages is of critical importance to bubble technology. Such testing must be thorough and flexible in diagnosing malfunctioning devices or characterizing new device designs, but also efficient and fast in routine tests for manufactured parts. The testing strategies, techniques, and equipment will continue to evolve. At present, two computer-controlled testing systems in industrial use have been reported by Bell Laboratories (see Hagedorn et al. [32]) and Texas Instruments (see Ferrio et al. [33] and Naden [34]). The first system has been used to test more than 3000 5-cm diameter wafers (~10^{10} bits); about 10% for repertory dialers (20 μm period), 60% for 68 kbit major/minor loop devices (16 μm period), and 30% for 68 kbit single shift register chips

(16 μm period). The paper also reported that about 200 4-chip packages were tested. The second system is used for product test at Texas Instruments.

The paper by Hagedorn et al. is a good tutorial paper which describes hardware, software, test strategy, and representative results. A Hewlett-Packard 2100A minicomputer is at the heart of the testing system. On the one hand, it interfaces with a range of peripheral units for input, output, and storage of data and programs. On the other, via four communication channels, it interfaces with the bubble wafer and testing facilities. The first channel goes to a digital ohmmeter and a probe and stage controller which measure the resistance of the various conductors (generate, annihilate, replicate, transfer, sense). The second channel goes to a decoder which interprets all information from the computer for equipment setup (rotating field, bias field, pulse generators, strobed detector). The third channel transfers information from the computer to the bubble array to set up the desired information pattern. The fourth channel is a programmable digital waveform recorder which allows the comparison of the detector waveform with any specifications stored in the computer.

The software contains the input/output routines which establish the test parameters and record the test results. It also includes an executive program which defines the overall test strategy and is largely composed of calls to various hardware-activating subroutines interspersed with logical decisions from the computer after it has received results from subroutine execution.

The testing usually proceeds from (1) quick screening measurements to eliminate defective chips to (2) detailed margin curve measurements on remaining chips varying the critical parameters, and then to (3) longevity tests and start/stop tests.

Experience with major/minor loop chip testing indicates that the rotating-field amplitude and replication-current-pulse phase and amplitude are most critical parameters and subject to processing and design variations. The longevity test examines the degradation of bias field margin with the increase of field rotation cycles. In the start and stop test, the bias field is set near the upper or lower limit, and the rotating field is typically operated for the order of 10^6 cycles and is stopped and started periodically so that the complicated data pattern stored in the chip stops in every conceivable way on each element of the propagation circuit.

CURRENT PRODUCTS

The current bubble products range from a 92 kbit major/minor loop memory module suitable for microprocessors to a 10^8-bit multiple-module serial store intended for use in spacecraft recording in 1978-1979. Although Hitachi announced a bubble product in 1975 and Rockwell in 1976, bubbles did not become a commercial reality until 1977 when TI introduced its products in the open market.

Western Electric's Announcement System and Serial Bubble Store [35]

The various announcement systems at Western Electric in its customer premises and central office installations in the past have been implemented by several audio magnetic drum designs: a movable head for a single-channel variable message length service, multiple fixed heads to provide individual message channels or

TABLE 3
Western Electric 13A Announcement System Characteristics

Capacity	$8 \times 272,484$ bits (2 for fixed-length message and 6 for variable length message)
Format	4 shift registers in series
Data rate	24 kbits/sec
Interface	TTL
Voltages	-4, +5, -8, ±14, -48 V
Power dissipation	–
Volume	21.5" × 12" × 9"
Temperature	0 to 50°C (operating) -40 to 80°C (idle)
Weight	–

message segments, etc. The mechanical drums require periodic maintenance and suffer message quality deterioration.

The 32-pin dual-in-line 4-chip bubble memory module (272,484 bits) [8] offers attractive components for a large portion of the central office recorded announcement systems, which requires many messages less than 12 sec long, with the balance of longer and variable length.

Adaptive Delta Modulation (ADM) permits the digital encoding, storage, and retrieval of speech with good fidelity at 24 kbits/sec. Four 68-kbit shift registers in a package connected in series store 12 sec worth of message. A variable length channel with up to 24 sec recording can be composed of two packages with message length increments of 3 sec. In Table 3 the essential characteristics of the WE 13A Announcement System are summarized. Also refer to Fig. 7 which is a photograph of the 13A Announcement System. The 3 boards on the left contain power converter, control, and field generation. The additional 8 boards are channel modules in any combination of fixed and/or variable message lengths. The system permits recording locally or from a remote location through a dedicated Call Director, and the dubbing of a professionally recorded tape. The components on the boards are further detailed in Fig. 8, and a detailed explanation is given by Williams [35]. The drive and detector circuits are described by Radner and Wuorinen [24].

The Serial Bubble Store is essentially based on the same bubble chips used in the Announcement System, and is intended to replace magnetic tape peripheral systems. It is for system applications requiring electrically alterable, nonvolatile, sequential stores, such as in backup for volatile RAM and program paging operations. Its portability enables physical transfer of programs or data, and its simple TTL interface requires minimal microprocessor (controller) firmware. The system is superior to magnetic tapes and suitable for use in microprocessor-based applications. The essential characteristics and physical appearance are shown in Table 4 and Fig. 9, respectively. Its system organization and operation are depicted in Fig. 10.

We shall only mention some features, leaving the details to the original papers [35, 36]. The customer-supplied system clock (960 kHz) provides the rotating field rate (48 kHz after dividing 960 kHz by 20) and all other system timing (for generate, replicate, transfer, and detection within each field cycle). The main shift register

FIG. 7. 13A Announcement System—front cover open. (After Williams [35], Fig. 7.)

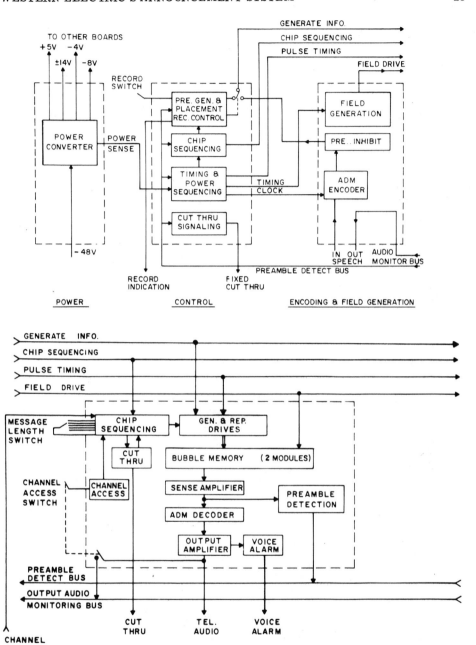

FIG. 8. 13A Announcement System—circuit diagram. The four sections consist of power, control, encoding and field generation, and incrementally-variable message channels (12 to 24 sec). (After Williams [35], Figs. 3 and 5.)

TABLE 4
Western Electric Serial-Bubble-Store Characteristics

Capacity	272,484 bits
Format	4 selectable shift registers
Data rate	48 kbits/sec
Interface	TTL
Voltages	+5, ±15 V
Power dissipation	–
Volume	–
Temperature	0 to 50°C (operating)
	–40 to 80°C (idle)
Weight	–

(68,121 bits) is preceded by an 8-bit register and followed by a 60-bit register. Input data enters all four 8-bit registers, but the decoder only enables the transfer conductor to write into the main loop in one chip. The data normally circulate in the main register. Only when Write or Read Enable is asserted, data are routed into an output 60-bit shift register which leads to the magnetoresistive detector. Nonvolatility is achieved by on-board circuitry which monitors all power supplies. Any out-of-limit voltage condition results in the shutdown of the field coil drive voltages in a prescribed manner.

FIG. 9. Serial Bubble Store. (After Williams [35], Fig. 8.)

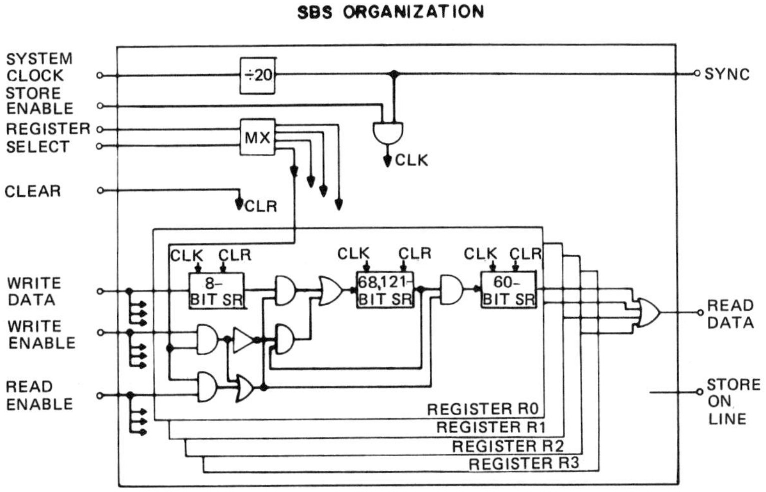

SBS ORGANIZATION

FIG. 10. Serial Bubble Store organization. Four shift registers in parallel. Each 68 kbit shift register has an 8-bit input buffer and a 60-bit output buffer. (After Williams [35], Fig. 9.)

Current Government Programs

Before discussing Rockwell's and Texas Instrument's products, it is appropriate to summarize a recent review of space and military applications of bubbles [37]. Tables 5-7 present a summary from Ref. 37.

TABLE 5
Space and Military Applications

Airborne—computer mass memory
Airborne data input "cassette"
Digital data recorders—spaceborne, sonabuoy
Spaceborne computer mass memory
Instrumentation recorders—airborne, missile, test sled
Shipboard/submarine computer mass memory
Airborne warning, command, control
Airborne surveillance systems
Ground based—command, control, communications
New digital avionics microprocessor based systems

TABLE 6
DOD Requirements

	Fast access mass memory	Digital recorder
Capacity	15 to 300 Mbits	10 to 10^3 Mbits
Weight	10 to 200 lb	10 to 30 lb
Data rate	1 to 8 Mbits/sec	1 to 10 Mbits/sec
Access time	1 to 10 msec	Seconds
MTBF	1000's of hours	10,000's of hours
Cost	0.5 to 0.05¢/bit	0.5 to 0.01¢/bit
Power	10 to 500 W	10 to 100 W
Temperature range	At least -25 to +75°C	At least -25 to +75°C
Radiation hardening	Use dependent	Use dependent
Nonvolatility	Required	Required

TABLE 7
Comparison with Commercial Requirements

Common to commercial
 1. Nonvolatile
 2. Low cost
 3. Large capacities
 4. Low power

Special for military
 1. Extremely small size and low weight
 2. High untended reliability
 3. Extremely low power—zero power stand-by
 4. Environmental:
   Shock/vibration
   -25 to +75°C or better
   Radiation-hard
   Minimized gyro effects
   Vacuum/zero "g" capabilities

The industrial development of bubble technology has been nurtured and enhanced significantly by government contracts. Two current major programs will be mentioned.

1. The Air Force Avionics Laboratory began a major contract effort at Texas Instruments in June 1975 to develop and fabricate several magnetic bubble memory "brassboard" systems. The data module consists of eight two-chip (major/minor loops) dual-in-line packages, which stores 2×10^6 bits at a data I/O rate of 2 MHz. Each package has a volume of 6.3 cm^3, weighs 28 g, and runs at 250 kHz. A follow-up program for the above is two 16×10^6 bit disk/

drum type systems (0.025 m^3, 25 kg) and two 10^8 bit recorder type systems, both using the 2×10^6 bit data modules as standard storage cards.

2. NASA at Langley Research Center began the development of a magnetic bubble data recorder at Rockwell in October 1975. The program aims at a 10^8-bit recorder for spacecraft (see below in the section entitled Rockwell's Solid-State Data Recorder and POS-8).

The Air Force has also initiated the following:

2nd generation: 1 to 2 μm bubble, gap-tolerant overlay, 16×10^6 bit fast-access memory at 10 lb (4.5 kg), and 10^9 bit recorder at 30 lb (14 kg).
3rd generation: 2-layer bubble lattice, self-biasing, full wafer, 10^{12} bit memory.

Rockwell's Solid-State Data Recorder and POS-8

Data storage is an essential function in most spacecrafts to provide either a mass storage to compensate for inadequate information transfer links, or a buffer storage to regulate flow of information, or a transient storage to permit preprocessing of information prior to transmission. The most cost effective storage on board spacecraft today is the magnetic tape recorder. Due to the presence of moving parts in such recorders, failure rates are as high as 1 per 10^4 hr of operation. In view of the criticality of the data storage function in space missions, the National Aeronautics and Space Administration has sponsored sizable efforts at Rockwell International to develop a large capacity (10^8 bits) magnetic bubble spacecraft recorder. A prototype is being readied for use in space in 1978. The recorder could be one of the first bubble-memory systems to operate in space. Moreover, it could also be one of the bubble-memory systems offering truly large capacity to vie with fixed-head magnetic disk files.

TABLE 8
Solid-State Data Recorder Characteristics

Capacity	104,857,600 bits
Format	
Serial	1-4 channels
Parallel	1, 8-bit byte
Data rate/channel	1.2 MHz
Maximum data rate	2.4 MHz
Access time	0.5 sec
Fill or dump time	1.0 sec
MTBF	4×10^4 hr
Interface	TTL
Voltage	28 ± 4 V
Power	103 W maximum at 100% duty cycle and linearly variable with duty cycle and data rate
Volume	860 in.^{3} ($5.3 \times 12.7 \times 12.75$)
Weight	47 lb

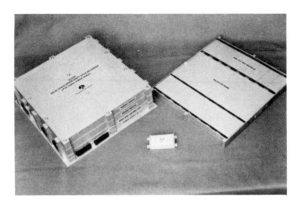

FIG. 11. A mock-up of the Solid-State Data Recorder—600 in.^{3}, 40 lb, 100 W max. (After Mavity [41], Fig. 1.)

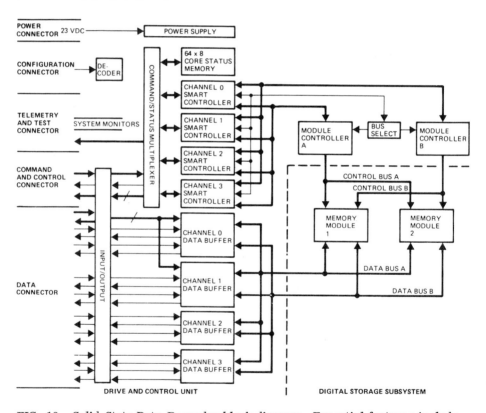

FIG. 12. Solid-State Data-Recorder block diagram. Essential features include reconfiguration capabilities, dual buses, override of failed cells, and full status monitoring. (After Mavity [41], Fig. 2.)

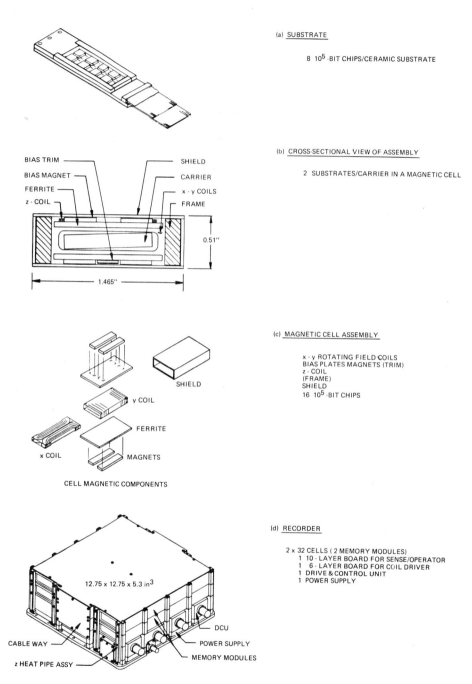

(a) <u>SUBSTRATE</u>

8 10^5 -BIT CHIPS/CERAMIC SUBSTRATE

(b) <u>CROSS-SECTIONAL VIEW OF ASSEMBLY</u>

2 SUBSTRATES/CARRIER IN A MAGNETIC CELL

BIAS TRIM
BIAS MAGNET
FERRITE
z - COIL
SHIELD
CARRIER
x - y COILS
FRAME
0.51"
1.465"

(c) <u>MAGNETIC CELL ASSEMBLY</u>

x - y ROTATING FIELD COILS
BIAS PLATES MAGNETS (TRIM)
z - COIL
(FRAME)
SHIELD
16 10^5 -BIT CHIPS

SHIELD
y COIL
FERRITE
x COIL
MAGNETS
CELL MAGNETIC COMPONENTS

(d) <u>RECORDER</u>

2 x 32 CELLS (2 MEMORY MODULES)
1 10 - LAYER BOARD FOR SENSE/OPERATOR
1 6 - LAYER BOARD FOR COIL DRIVER
1 DRIVE & CONTROL UNIT
1 POWER SUPPLY

12.75 x 12.75 x 5.3 in^3
DCU
CABLE WAY
POWER SUPPLY
MEMORY MODULES
z HEAT PIPE ASSY

FIG. 13. Solid-State Data-Recorder assembly: (a) substrate, (b) cross-sectional view, (c) components in a cell, and (d) recorder. (After Becker and Stermer [22].)

A series of papers documenting the development of the solid-state data recorder has been presented by Chen et al. [38], Hoffman et al. [39], Becker and Stermer [22], and Stermer [40].

The essential characteristics of the recorder are summarized in Table 8, and a mock-up model is photographed in Fig. 11. The system organization is presented in Fig. 12 and the packaging is depicted in Fig. 13.

The recorder consists of two memory modules each having 32 cells, each cell containing 16 100-kbit single shift-register bubble memory chips. The cell, being the basic memory assembly unit, has been designed to contain all the required magnetic, thermal, and structural components. In assembling cells into magnetic modules, matrix selection and sharing of sense amplifiers are used to achieve close packing. The memory modules are interconnected to a drive and control unit module which contains four microprocessors, 500 integrated circuits, a RAM core memory, and two PROM's.

Several factors which contribute to the system reliability will be mentioned. The intrinsic nonvolatility property permits true start-stop operation with zero power consumption in the standby mode. In addition, the start-stop mode eliminates cumulative errors which would result from the circulation or refreshing of data in the standby mode. Since the entire memory is divided into 64 cells, should any cell fail, the system loses only 1.5% of its capacity. Thus the MTBF of the system is 40,000 hr but the usability of the memory extends far beyond the system MTBF.

The system also offers flexible architecture. It can be configured to provide one memory of 10^8 bits to four memories of 25×10^6 bits each. It also provides dual bus throughput, override of failed cells in steps 1.5% of total capacity, and full status monitoring.

The Rockwell POS-8 utilizes the same 102,300 bit single shift-register bubble chips as in the NASA recorder. It is organized as eight parallel endless loops (i.e., 8 chips in parallel), and useful as a mass memory for a microprocessor. The essential characteristics are shown in Table 9. It is of interest to note its variable buffering speed (from dc to 100 kHz), and variable power consumption. At peak speed (and power), the memory can be filled or emptied in 1 sec. When idle, no power is dissipated. In many applications the duty cycle is much less than 1% and battery power can be conserved.

TABLE 9
POS/8 Characteristics

Capacity	819,200 bits
Format	Endless loop/byte parallel
Data rate	100 kbytes/sec
	800 kbits/sec
Interface	TTL
Voltages	±5, +32V ±2%
Power dissipation	29 W maximum at 100% duty cycle and linearly variable with duty cycle
Volume	50 in.³ ≈ 820 cm³
Temperature	0 to 50°C
Weight	2.5 lb ≈ 1.14 kg

FIG. 14. POS/8 bubble memory. (After Mavity [41], Fig. 3.)

The module as shown in Fig. 14 contains the magnetic memory and all the associated clocking, coil drive, and read/write electronics. The design was predicated upon extensive use of readily available components. The interface to the user provides TTL compatible commands, data paths, and clocks, which can be easily integrated to a system through a simple controller.

The block diagram is shown in Fig. 15. The memory operation is straightforward. Enabling the select line brings the memory to operational readiness and starts the clock. Start/stop set to TRUE starts the data circulating and enables a

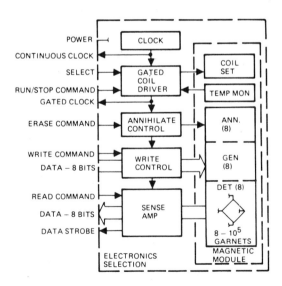

FIG. 15. POS/8 block diagram. (After Mavity [41], Fig. 4.)

gated clock that occurs at the beginning of each cycle. Coincident TRUES on combinations of Read, Write, and/or Erase effect read, write and/or erase. As endless loops of data, the addressing is left to the user to format. Fixed, variable, or unique block addressing via data header or counters can be implemented. Note that the approach here is to make the bubble memory emulate disk tracks and tape loops.

Mavity [41] describes a range of potential applications for POS-8 like bubble memory, which are based on the following properties of the bubble memory:

Portability (low power, small size and weight, simplicity and ruggedness)
Radiation hardness
Nonvolatility
Fast access

In military applications the portability allows the updating of remote computing system such as reconfiguring an aircraft for a different navigational or fire control mission. Its low power enables its use in gathering remote, passive intelligence, or as an on-demand event recorder to gather seismic data. In industrial applications its portability makes it attractive as a memory for a desk-top calculator and for an electronic notebook (recording and reconfiguring of transactions). Its fast access and small size make it suitable as on-line secondary storage for microprocessors, thus extending the capability of memory hierarchy and multiprogramming to microprocessors. It is also useful for stand-alone terminals, automated office equipment, and personal computers.

The design of the controller depends on several considerations such as the following:

Incremental record (started, cycled once for R/W, stopped) or block record
    (started, burst transfer, stopped)
Programmed I/O via CPU or direct memory access
Record identification (start, end, etc.) via ASCII codes or counting cycles from an
    index mark
Use of nondata characters such as longitudinal parity, cyclic redundancy codes,
    write protection codes, and supervisor key codes

Texas Instrument's Bubble Memory Module and Portable Memory Terminals

TBM 0103 Bubble Memory Module

As is amply clear from the description of various entry bubble products in the preceding sections, a major application is as mass memories for minicomputers and microcomputers.

The evolution of mass memories for minicomputers and microcomputers is summarized in Table 10. In essence, the smaller the storage capacity, the more rapidly the per-bit price of a disk file increases (e.g., 0.3¢/bit for 0.7 Mbit floppy, 0.07¢/bit for 6 Mbit floppy, 0.05¢/bit for 20 Mbit moving-head disk, and 0.005¢/bit for 800 Mbit moving-head disk). Even at their initial entry into the market place, bubble memories are already cost competitive with disks at less than 3 Mbit capacity. According to the manufacturers (e.g., Juliussen et al. [11]), the system price for a single bubble chip including interfacing circuitry should be as low as $75 in

TABLE 10
Chronology of Minicomputer Mass Memory
(after Juliussen et al. [11])

Year	Minicomputer	On-line memory	Off-line memory
1968	PDP 8: $13,000	Mainframe disk (IBM 2311 class): $25,000	Mainframe magnetic tape (IBM 2401 class): $20,000
1971	PDP 11, TI-960, 980: $8,000	Cartridge moving-head disk (Diablo 31): $10,000	Minicomputer magnetic tape: $9,000
1974	"Naked" minicomputer: < $3,000	Floppy disk: $3,000	Cassette: $2,000 3M cartridge: $3,000
1977	Microcomputer-on-a-board: < $1,000	Bubble memories, charge coupled device memories: $75 and up	Minicassette, mini-floppy: $1,000 and up

quantity in 1978 (0.07¢/bit). Moreover, the bubble module allows storage capacity to be tailored to size in small 92-kbit increments.

There has been a series of papers published by TI to explore bubble applications. They include Juliussen et al. [11, 12, 42], Lee [43], Naden and West [44], Bhandarkar and Juliussen [45].

At present, the TI module is a 25-g, $1.1 \times 1 \times 0.4$ in.^{3}, 0.5 W, 14-pin, dual-in-line package (complete with chip, drive coils, and bias magnets), and currently selling at $200 (or 0.2¢/bit). It distinguishes itself from its competitors in several respects. It uses major/minor loop organization to achieve 5 msec access time. It employs redundancy to improve yield (92 kbits useful out of 100 kbits on a chip). Its packaging and voltages are compatible with semiconductor components to share the printed circuit board of a microprocessor. An N-MOS controller module is available for interfacing with standard microprocessors.

The essential characteristics of TBM 0103 are summarized in Table 11. Detailed descriptions are available in the product literature [4, 46].

A typical microprocessor system design that uses bubble-memory mass storage is shown in Fig. 16. To perform a read operation, the CPU selects a bubble module from which to access data via the chip select logic, and then it loads the controller with a page number and gives the read command. Upon accessing the proper page, the controller stores the data in its buffers and interrupts the CPU, which then reads the data from the controller's buffer. Similarly, for a write operation, the CPU writes the data into the buffer of the controller, initiates the transfer, and waits for the controller to signal that data storage in the form of bubbles is completed.

Let us now describe the various components in the system of Fig. 16.

TABLE 11
Texas Instrument TBM 0103 Bubble Memory
Printed Circuit Evaluation Board Characteristics

Capacity	92,304 bits
Format	Major/minor loops: 157 minor loops, 641 periods/loop (144 useful, 13 spare)
Data rate	50 kbits/sec
Access time (1st bit)	4 msec
Cycle time (144-bit block)	12.8 msec
Interface	Microprocessor controller (TMS 9916) and TTL circuits
Voltages	±5, ±12 V
Power dissipation	0.6 W
Volume	$1.1 \times 1 \times 0.4$ in.^{3} (bubble module only)
Temperature	-40 to 85°C (operating -40 to 100°C (idle)
Weight	20 g (bubble module only)
Maximum permissible external field	40 Oe

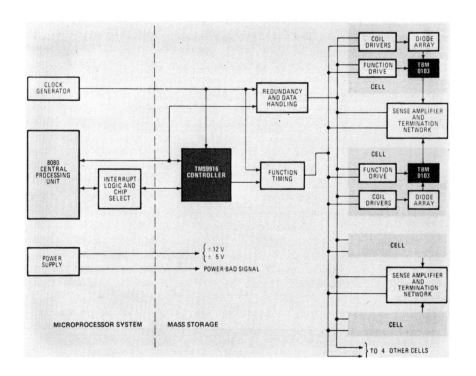

FIG. 16. A magnetic-bubble mass-storage memory for a microprocessor system. Up to 8 nonvolatile memory cells provide a maximum storage of 738,432 bits or 92,304 8-bit bytes. (After Juliussen et al. [11].)

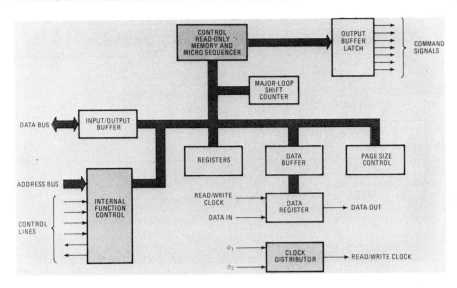

FIG. 17. TMS 9916 n-channel MOS controller chip. It controls the shifting of
bubbles, ensures their synchronization, and maintains page position information.
It also includes a mask-programmed ROM that can be programmed for different
loop organization. (After Juliussen et al. [11].)

Controller
    The TMS 9916 controller is shown in greater detail in Fig. 17. It starts and
stops bubble shifting, maintains page position information, and ensures synchronization with the bubble module. A 40-pin, n-channel MOS device, it contains a control ROM, serial/parallel conversion for data transfer on bubble chip, a 20-byte
buffer for temporary data storage, and addressing logic to maintain synchronization
with data shifting in the module. Software is used to set the controller for variable
page sizes of 1 to 20 bytes, variable minor-loop size of up to 1024 bits, and multipage transfer capability of 1 to 1024 pages. In response to commands from the
CPU, the controller enables the functions necessary to access a page or pages of
data in either a single-page or multipage mode. In the multipage mode, it accesses
long blocks of data a page at a time, and interrupt is generated after each byte is
read or written until the transfer is complete. In the single-page mode, a single
interrupt is generated at the end of the transfer. At the proper bubble field rotation
period, the controller sends flags to external circuitry that performs bubble operations such as annihilation or replication.

Redundancy and Data Handling
    The 13 unused minor loops (some defective) in each module are mapped into a
1024-bit programmable ROM (see Fig. 18). In operation, the map for an accessed
module is read from the ROM and is used to inhibit data transfer when necessary
to prevent bad bits from reaching the controlling buffer. There is also the possi-
bility of storing the map in the bubble device itself and to read it into CPU RAM
during system initialization.

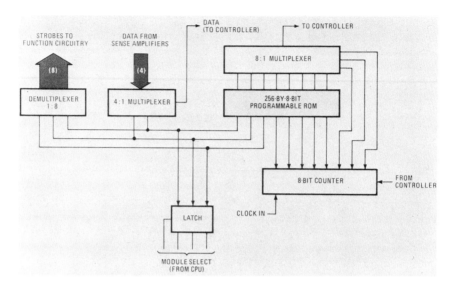

FIG. 18. Mapping of defective minor loops. A 1024-bit programming ROM stores the map of defective minor loops, and is used to check each bit of a page during its readout to remove any bad bit. (After Juliussen et al. [11].)

Controlling Function Timing

Function timing is controlled by a 22-pin low-power Schottky transistor-transistor-log chip that consists of control flip-flops that synchronize and control the starting, shifting, and stopping sequences of the bubble field rotation, a mask-programmable ROM that coordinates timing pulses and that may be changed to accommodate other chip architectures, and output latches and gates. The TTL-level signals are converted to constant drives on a separate 16-pin function-drive IC (transfer, annihilate, and generate), and to a triangular waveform coil drive current on a separate 8-pin IC in conjunction with a diode array.

The logic-level output upon the detection of a bubble is produced from two devices. One is an 8-pin hybrid-circuit termination network to provide two legs of the detection bridge. It also includes ac-coupling and high-frequency filtering components, and the current-setting resistors for the function-drive circuit. The second device is an 8-pin sense amplifier which receives mV-level analog signals from the termination network and delivers logic-level outputs.

Memory Modules

Each memory cell contains a bubble memory module and the equivalent of three 16-pin dual-in-line devices. Eight of these modules on a circuit board would provide a total of 738,432 bits or 92,304 bytes. The power requirements of the 8-cell system in both the standby and active modes are estimated to be 1 and 5.38 W, respectively. For details, refer to Table 14 on page 334.

The entire system needs 40 in.^{2} to accommodate the 8 modules (1 in.^{2} per IC, 1.5 in.^{2} per bubble module, on a 2-sided printed circuit board) and 10 in.^{2} for the controller and data-handler logic, totaling 50 in.^{2}. The system weighs 0.67 lb.

Several cautions must be exercised in designing such bubble memory systems. The bubble transfer conductor can be easily burnt out if the drive pulse exceeds specifications. Transients are intolerable in the various drives, and they are disabled during power cycling. The small bubble signal cannot tolerate long leads between the sense amplifier, detectors, and termination network, and also requires good filtering of power supplies and a good ground plane on the board. In case of field stops, the power supplies must remain on for a minimum of 12.8 msec to return the data in the major loop to the minor loops.

Texas Instruments Model 765 Portable Memory Terminal ($2995) and Model 763 Memory Send-Receive Terminal ($2695)

Each terminal comes standard with 20,000 bytes of nonvolatile bubble memory storage (i.e., two TBM 0103 modules), expandable to 80,000 bytes in 20,000 byte increments ($500 per). The Model 765 Terminal is portable with a built-in acoustic coupler. Compared to cassettes, paper tapes, or floppy disks, the bubble terminals have the advantage of electronic reliability, higher access speeds (15 msec instead of hundreds of msec for floppy disks), smaller size, and less weight and power consumption. The terminals allow data entry during daily use, off-line from the host computer. The stored data can then be transmitted to the home office computer over standard telephone lines at a speed of 30 characters per second (300 baud) via the built-in acoustic coupler, or at 120 characters per second when connected to an external modem. The terminals are equipped with ASCII keyboard, numeric cluster, thermal printer, self-test capability, and editing capability. The user can select communications options, configure memory, and enter or edit text. The applications include time sharing, real estate inquiry, newspaper reporting, wholesale and retail order entry and credit verification, and insurance inquiry.

The architecture of the terminals and their operational characteristics are described by Flannigan [47].

VERSATILITY OF SHIFT REGISTERS AND MAJOR/MINOR LOOPS

The first-generation bubble memory chips used in commercial products are long shift registers (16-kbit chips from Hitachi, 100-kbit chips from Rockwell, and 64-kbit chips from Western Electric) and major/minor loops (TI's 100-kbit chips). An interesting question to ask is what will be their product life. The first generation bubble chips typically use 4 to 5 μm bubble diameter ($\sim 1.5 \times 10^6$ bit/in.^{2}). Developments are well on the way to use 2 to 3 μm bubble diameters, higher densities ($\sim 6 \times 10^6$ bit/in.^{2}), and a larger chip capacity (256 kbits to 1 Mbit).

Moreover, the single long shift registers as well as the major/minor loops are amenable to reconfiguration to improve performance significantly. We shall impose the condition that only the existing components (e.g., shift elements, generators, switches) are to be used, and then demonstrate a number of novel chip configurations:

Long shift registers:
I/O buffers
Dynamic reallocation

Major/minor loops:
  Varieties of read/write arrangements
  Redundant loops
  Endless loop simulation
  On-chip hierarchy
  Cryptography

Input/Output Buffers

In the Bell System Serial Bubble Store, four single shift-register chips are connected in parallel. Each shift register has a 68,121-bit main recirculating loop which is preceded by an 8-bit input-buffer section and followed by a 60-bit output buffer section. Refer to Fig. 10. During write-in, identical data are entered into all the input buffers, but the select decoder activates only one chip to transfer data from its input buffer into its main loop. Similar selection is exercised with the readout.

Dynamic Reallocation

Programmers have long observed that, in data processing, the most recently used data are very likely to be reused soon. They have taken advantage of this fact by constructing algorithms which arrange data in the order of how recently they have been used. Such an algorithm can be implemented in hardware by using bubble domain devices (Beausoleil et al. [48] and Bonyhard and Nelson [49]).

Essential to the dynamic ordering is the ability to shift forward all bits until the bit currently referred to is in the foremost (output) position. The bit is frozen there while the other bits are restored. This can be accomplished by allowing bubbles to propagate in two directions, corresponding to clockwise and counterclockwise field rotations. The reverse direction of propagation leaves the foremost bit at the output position. See Fig. 19(a). One embodiment of the bidirectional dynamic-ordering shift register is shown in Fig. 19(b). Alternatively, unidirectional propagation (by Permalloy pattern) can be aided with local current loops [137]. See Fig. 19(c). The Permalloy pattern is used to propagate all bits. The current loops are used to freeze the bubble at the foremost position and to bridge over the gap opened by the frozen position in the Permalloy path. The second scheme obviates the need for fast-reversing field coils.

In a dynamically ordered shift register array, a word distributes its bits among the different shift registers. Moreover, each word carries its own address, which moves with the information bits of the word (see Fig. 20). When an address appears in the address register, the bits in the shift registers are first propagated clockwise. With each step of propagation, the address of the foremost word is compared with the desired address, and the total number of steps advanced (n) is recorded by a counter. The clockwise propagation is continued until the desired address is found. Then the rotating field is reversed, and the bubbles are propagated in the counterclockwise direction by (n - 1) steps. The process of dynamic ordering is illustrated in Fig. 21.

Bonyhard and Nelson [49] have presented a model which relates the dynamically ordered shift-register memory to stack processing, a technique used in the

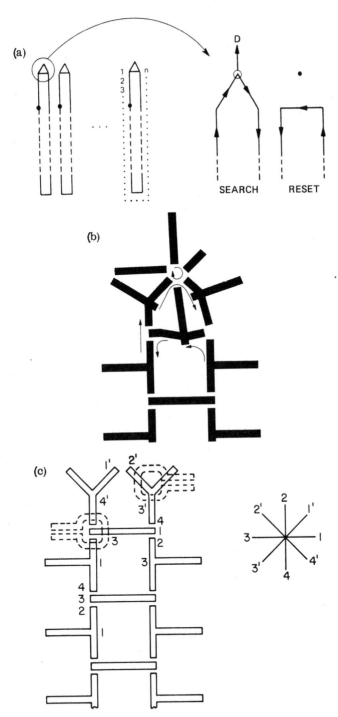

FIG. 19. Shift register loops for dynamic address reallocation. (a) Search and reset. (b) Permalloy patterns (bidirectional). (c) Permalloy patterns (unidirectional, aided with current loop). (After Bonyhard and Nelson [49], Figs. 1 and 2; and Lee et al. [137], Fig. 1.)

39

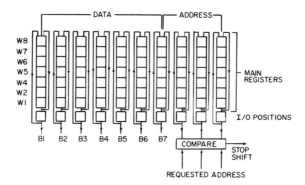

FIG. 20. A dynamically ordered shift register array reduces the effective access time to a value approaching the field rotation period. (After Chang [88], Fig. 3.)

evaluation of memory hierarchies. The technique also enables the optimization of memory design based on the traces of selected typical programs. For a 2-Mbit bubble memory with 128 detectors (i.e., 16 Kbit/detector), in executing the type of programs for which trace data are available, an average of only 8.8 shifts per access and an average of 12.1 shifts per memory cycle are required. If bubbles are propagated at a data rate of 1 MHz, the average access and cycle times for this memory become 8.8 and 12.1 μsec, respectively, which are highly competitive with large-capacity main memories of cores and semiconductors. This memory, when operated in conjunction with a faster buffer (say 64 kbit, 0.5 μsec access time, 1 μsec cycle time), will further reduce the average number of shifts per access to 1.05, and the average number of shifts per cycle to 1.9.

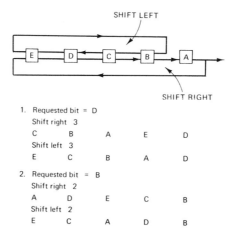

FIG. 21. An illustration of the dynamic ordering process. The initial order is ABCDE. After the requests for D and B, the order becomes BDACE. (After Chang [88], Fig. 4.)

Beausoleil et al. [48] have also considered a double ordering scheme and a two-dimensional ordering scheme for additional performance improvement.

Varieties of Read/Write Arrangements

Although bubbles have been labeled as electronic disk files, there is very limited analogy between the two technologies. See Fig. 22. Disks, particularly large ones with long tracks, lack modularity and depend on data formatting on the structureless tracks to define data structure, ensure data reliability, and provide intelligence for the data. By contrast, bubbles are structured storage arrays. They are highly modular, and can have data structure, reliability (e.g., via redundancy), and intelligence designed into the array configuration.

The major/minor loop array has several variations in its I/O arrangements. From the hardware designer's viewpoint, the type of switches available dictates the I/O arrangement. Depending on whether the transfer switch is unidirectional or bidirectional, two or one major loop must be provided. If the transfer switch cannot replicate, replication before detection and rewrite capability must be provided. If the transfer switch cannot execute transfer/clear in addition to replicate/transfer by adjusting the transfer current level, additional clearing means will be needed. All the above variations will result in different path lengths of the input and output, as well as the timing of the read and write.

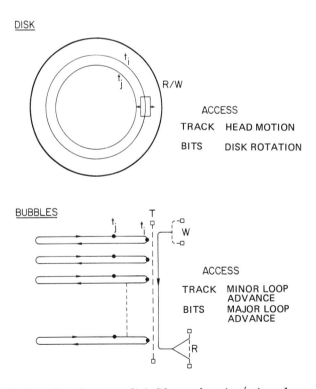

FIG. 22. Limited analogy between disk files and major/minor loops.

From the user's viewpoint, he desires

1. To minimize the access time
2. To minimize the read time
3. To minimize the read/write cycle time
4. To read out bits from a word continuously
5. To read the same word repeatedly
6. To read and write long records without gap
7. To read and write simultaneously
8. To be able to read, modify, and write

It might be conjectured that not all requirements will be satisfied simultaneously.

Let us first analyze the array in Fig. 23 (also see Fig. 4). Bidirectional nonreplicate switches are used for data transfer between the major and minor loops. No field reversal ability is assumed. Thus, in the worst case situation when the

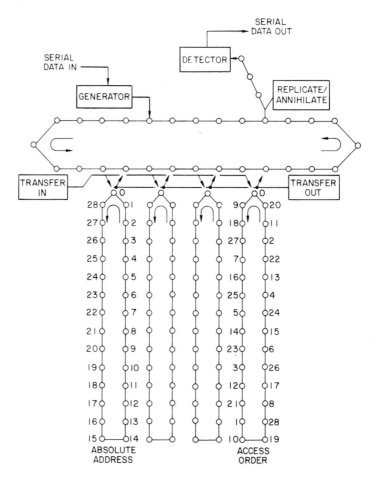

FIG. 23. Analysis of delays in a major/minor loop array. (After TI [4], Fig. 8.0.2.1.)

desired data have just been propagated beyond the transfer gates, they must be moved around the entire minor loops before transfer.

Access time = delay in minor loops
+ delay between 1st transfer switch and replicate
+ delay for amplification

For the TI 0103 bubble chip, the three delays are, respectively, 0 to 641 steps, 68 steps, and 86 steps.

Given a constant bit capacity (C) for a chip, and with n the number of minor loops, then

Access time = C/n + const (2nd and 3rd terms)

C/n is the length of the minor loop which is the worst-case delay. Obviously large number of short minor loops will result in short access time.

Read time for the word = access time + 2 × word length

$$= C/n + 2n + const$$

The factor 2 enters since the doubled-up minor loops only permit the bit from each minor loop to fill every other bit position in the major loop. When the read time is minimized with respect to n, the array consists of $n = (C/2)^{\frac{1}{2}}$ minor loops, each with $(2C)^{\frac{1}{2}}$ bits, yielding

Minimum read time = $2(2C)^{\frac{1}{2}}$ + const (worst case)

The dimension of the array is $2(C/2)^{\frac{1}{2}} \cdot 0.5(2C)^{\frac{1}{2}} = 2(C/2)^{\frac{1}{2}} \cdot (C/2)^{\frac{1}{2}}$; i.e., a 2 by 1 rectangle.

Read/write cycle time = retrieval delay in minor loops
+ read delay
+ write delay

$$= C/n + (2n + const\ 1) + (2n + const\ 2)$$

$$= C/n + 4n + const$$

Note that 4n approximates the total length of the closed major loop. When the cycle time is minimized with respect to n, the array consists of $C^{\frac{1}{2}}/2$ minor loops and $2C^{\frac{1}{2}}$ bits per minor loop, yielding

Minimum read/write cycle time (worst case) = $4C^{\frac{1}{2}}$

The dimension of the array is $C^{\frac{1}{2}} \cdot C^{\frac{1}{2}}$; i.e., a square. We see that for a single major loop array which requires rewrite, there is conflict in optimizing the geometry for minimum read time and for minimum read/write cycle time.

A word, when transferred into the major loop, can be read repeatedly by recirculating it through the replicator in the major loop. Due to the rewrite delay intervening between successive reads, there will always be gaps even when a long record to be read nondestructively is continuous. Since a word occupies every other bit position in the major loop, it is possible to interleave a read word and a write word in the common major loop to facilitate operations. The propagation delay between replicate and write stations is designed to exceed the amplification

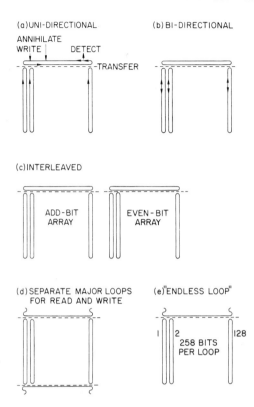

FIG. 24. Improvements of major/minor loops to achieve speed advantages.
(a) TI TBM 0103 chip. (b) Bidirectional shift registers. (c) Two major loops.
(d) Interleaved arrays. (e) Replicate transfer.

delay between replicate and detect stations, so that the new write data can be based
on the read data.

Let us now consider what array features will satisfy the user's requirements.
Refer to Fig. 24.

Minimum Access Time

Preferably the minor loops are capable of bidirectional propagation so that no
more than half of the minor loop needs to be traversed in accessing data. In addition, the entry to the amplifier/detector should be located as closely as possible to
the leading bit in the major loop. The delay for amplification could be reduced to
one field rotation period when the amplification is not executed by the multistep
chevron expander but by a synchronized multistage one-step compressor-amplifier
(a concept advanced by Beausoleil and Keefe, see Chang [9, p. 207]).

An alternative way to reduce access time is to provide short buffer loops
between the minor loops and the major loop, such as proposed by Pohm et al. [50].
Preselection of data can be performed, and such data can be placed in the buffer
loops such that as soon as the transfer interface is clear, such data can be transferred to the major loop.

Minimum Read Time

As derived in the above, the worst-case minimum read time is $2(2C)^{\frac{1}{2}}$ + constant in a 2×1 rectangular array.

Minimum Read/Write Cycle Time

As derived in the above, the worst-case minimum read/write cycle time is $4C^{\frac{1}{2}}$ in a square array. There could be different arrangements of the major loop(s). For example, two major loops could be provided, at opposite edges of the minor loops, one for read, and the other for write.

Continuous Readout

It has been mentioned that only every other bit position in the major loop is occupied after data transfer from the minor loops. Coincidentally, to avoid interaction between successive stripes (stretched bubbles) in the bubble expander, only every other bit position is utilized. In order to make a chip present a continuous bit data stream to the outside, two major/minor loop arrays can be accommodated on the same chip, one to handle odd bits and the other even bits, in their respective major loops. The two generators are activated alternatively to feed the two write major loops. The two detectors of the two read major loops are connected to the same sense amplifier so that their outputs will be interleaved. When the interaction between successive stripes is eliminated by suitable designs, two major loops from two arrays can supply odd and even bit streams to the same expander/detector.

Repeated Read

In order to be able to read the same word repeatedly without time lapse, the transfer switches in the read major loop should be of the replicate type, and the minor loop length should be equal to the read major loop length $[2n = C/n$, or $n = (C/2)^{\frac{1}{2}}]$. For the optimum array (see Minimum Read Time above), the minimum worst-case read time is $2(2C)^{\frac{1}{2}}$ + const. For the present array

Read time = $C/n + 2n$ + const

$\qquad$ = $4n$ + const

$\qquad$ = $2.82(C)^{\frac{1}{2}}$ + const

Gapless Long Records

In order to read gapless long records, the minor loop length should exceed the major loop length by one bit. Thus each time a word has been read, the minor loops present the next word for transfer. Stated more generally, a mutually prime-number ratio between minor loop length (expressed in number of bits) and major loop length will ensure continuous recording [51]. Moreover, the array will appear as an endless loop. For example, 513 records each of 128 bits can be written into 128 minor loops each containing 513 bits (a total of 56,664 bits).

Simultaneous Read and Write

Simultaneous read and write of different words should present no problem when two separate major loops are provided. Of course, only the locations accessible to the major loops at the same time can be read out and written into respectively and simultaneously. However, for the same word location which is not static but in circulation in the minor loops, not until the complete word (already transferred to the major loop) has been read and a decision made as to retention or modification of the word can the write operation be initiated.

Read, Modify, and Write

Naturally, the new word can be constructed based on the word just read, or logic functions performed with the word just read.

Cryptographic Memory [52]

Refer to Fig. 25. The memory is bit-organized; i.e., the bits in a word are distributed among many chips, one per chip. There is a major/minor loop array on each chip. For the purpose of encrypting and decrypting, the magnetic patterns of the major loop are superimposed by not only the transfer conductor pattern, but also by an inhibiting conductor pattern. When activated, the inhibiting conductor will prevent bubble advance in the major loop it controls.

For encrypting, a security key is selectively applied to some chips, which inhibits the advances of bubbles by a certain number of steps respectively in these chips. When unauthorized readout is attempted, readout would be meaningless

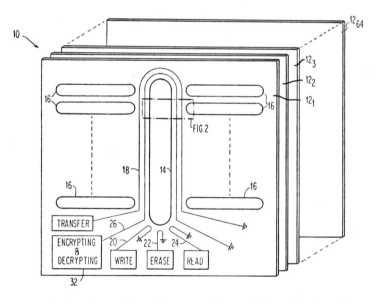

FIG. 25. Major/minor loop chip with encrypting and decrypting conductor superimposed on the major loop. (After Lin et al. [52], Figs. 1 and 2.)

without the necessary decryption. Only when the encrypted words are restored to their original states according to the security key can the data be read out meaningfully.

As an example, consider a block of data

$$b_{1,1} \quad\quad b_{1,2} \quad\quad b_{1,3} \quad\quad \cdots \quad\quad b_{1,256}$$

$$b_{2,1} \quad\quad b_{2,2} \quad\quad b_{2,3} \quad\quad \cdots \quad\quad b_{2,256}$$

$$\vdots$$

$$b_{64,1} \quad\quad b_{64,2} \quad\quad b_{64,3} \quad\quad \cdots \quad\quad b_{64,256}$$

The security key specifies that the second, fifth, and sixty-fourth major loops will have three shifts suppressed. The encrypted data will appear as follows:

$$b_{1,254} \quad\quad b_{1,255} \quad\quad b_{1,256} \quad\quad \cdots \quad\quad b_{1,253}$$

$$b_{2,1} \quad\quad b_{2,2} \quad\quad b_{2,3} \quad\quad \cdots \quad\quad b_{2,256}$$

$$b_{3,254} \quad\quad b_{3,255} \quad\quad b_{3,256} \quad\quad \cdots \quad\quad b_{3,253}$$

$$b_{4,254} \quad\quad b_{4,255} \quad\quad b_{4,256} \quad\quad \cdots \quad\quad b_{4,253}$$

$$b_{5,1} \quad\quad b_{5,2} \quad\quad b_{5,3} \quad\quad \cdots \quad\quad b_{5,256}$$

$$\vdots$$

$$b_{64,1} \quad\quad b_{64,2} \quad\quad b_{64,3} \quad\quad \cdots \quad\quad b_{64,256}$$

Note that encryption (or decryption) will require a major-loop cycle in addition to write (or read) operation.

A Fast Search Memory [53]

While the addresses of words are implied in their relative positions in the minor loops, it is also possible to allocate some minor loops to hold address codes and other minor loops to hold corresponding data. Such a memory will be almost immune to power failure, since it will only lose the data integrity of the word in the major loop while all data in minor loops will maintain their addresses. Moreover, such a memory, when properly organized, will allow much faster search for selected addresses.

Figure 26 shows a sketch of the memory organization. Accesses are provided separately for the address minor loops and for the data minor loops, as actuated by the separate replicate circuits. During search, only the much shorter address codes are read out consecutively and compared with the specified address, thus allowing much quicker identification of the desired data. Note that the address and data minor loops are synchronized with each other. Afterwards, only the identified data will be read out.

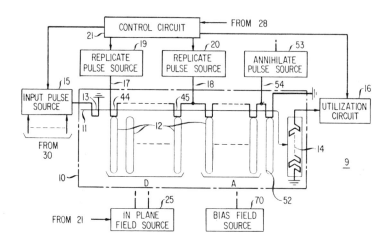

FIG. 26. A major/minor loop chip with the minor loops divided into two separately-addressable groups (address and data) so as to facilitate fast search. (After Bobeck and Fischer [53], Fig. 1.)

FORECAST FOR LSI BUBBLES

    The viability and longevity of a new technology obviously depend on its cost and performance relative to other technologies, and on the possibility for new applications. This section is to study (1) the historical trend and economic nature of semiconductor LSI in order to shed light on the bubble technology, (2) the approaches to high-density bubble devices in terms of device structures, materials, and lithographies, (3) the dependence of device properties on scaling, (4) the status and projection of the storage market, and (5) the competition with semiconductor CCD's and magnetic disks. The performance aspects will be addressed below in the sections entitled Subsystems, Architectures, and Programming, and Performance.

Historical Trends of LSI Semiconductor Devices

    In recent articles by Moore [54] and Noyce [55], the historical trend was reviewed and future improvements were examined for the semiconductor technology in terms of cost, reliability, and performance in an effort to assess whether the IC technology is entering its maturity or dotage, or is still on the upbeat.
    Given that magnetic bubble technology is also an LSI technology, their analysis provides guidance for bubbles as well. In particular, we shall bring out the relevant bubbles aspects to augment their analysis.
    For a given device configuration and cell size, after amortization of design cost, the production costs are determined by the chip processing cost (Si or garnet wafers plus device structures) and the assembly/test cost. The chip cost is affected by the yield which is determined by the probability of defects in the aggregate of components on the chip. The assembly process is to put a tiny chip in a housing which includes a mechanical transition from the IC microscopic interconnections

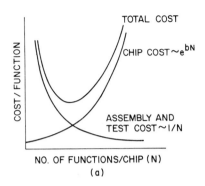

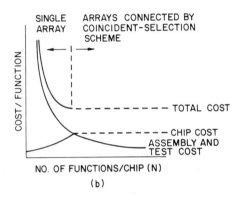

FIG. 27. Cost/function vs circuit complexity (i.e., number of functions per chip). (a) For single array (after Noyce [55], Fig. 1). (b) For multiple arrays connected with coincident selection.

to circuit board lead dimensions (e.g., from 10 to 2500 μm). The IC chip design usually takes care to increase chip bit capacity without significant increase of the number of interconnections. Figure 27 shows the cost/function for processor chips or cost/bit for memory chips as a function of number of bits per chip. The manufacturing strategy obviously should aim at minimum total cost.

The chip complexity (i.e., components per chip) at the minimum cost point has been steadily improving with time. Figure 28 shows the historical trend. The circuit complexity has been doubling per year for nearly two decades (or increasing by 10^3 times per decade). The economical advantage is roughly a 10^2 times decrease in cost-per-bit for a 10^3 times increase in chip complexity. It is a very significant question to ask whether the same pace of progress will be sustained in the years and decades ahead. According to Moore [54], the factors contributing to the improvement are:

Device and circuit cleverness	100
Dimension reduction	32
Die size (or chip size) increase	20

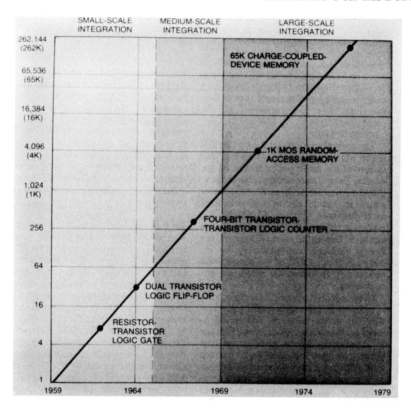

FIG. 28. IC chip capacity vs time. The number of components per chip doubles every year. (After Noyce [55], Fig. 2.)

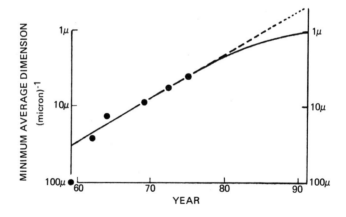

FIG. 29. Minimum average dimension vs time. (After Noyce [55], Fig. 3.)

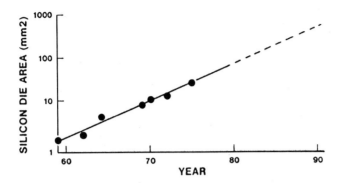

FIG. 30. Silicon die area vs time. (After Noyce [55], Fig. 4.)

The numbers indicate individual contributions of the three factors to chip complexity improvement from 1959 to 1975, resulting in the net advance from single transistor to 64-kbit chip.

To support Moore's analysis, let us recall that the semiconductor memory cell has evolved from the early six-transistor cell to one-transistor cell to IC capacitors (CCD's). However, these dramatic improvements are probably leveling off. In fact, a major concern of the semiconductor industry at present is the lack of obvious ways to further simplify one-transistor cell and CCD's, and to prevent the leveling-off of the curve in Fig. 28. The lithography improvement with time is depicted in Fig. 29, and the die size (i.e., chip size) improvement with time is depicted in Fig. 30.

Let us now return to Figs. 27 and 28 to examine the benefits of more components per chip. In terms of cost, there is reduction not only for the immediate chip-module assembly and test, but also for the subsequent assembly into computer hardware since more interconnections are made within the IC components; there is smaller equipment, fewer cabinets, and cables; and there is reduced power and cooling. The replacement of chip level interconnections (solder joints or connectors) by interconnections within chips contribute significantly to reliability as well.

Development Forecast for LSI Bubble Devices

Magnetic bubbles are just emerging in the marketplace. Much innovation in devices and circuits beyond the present T-bar Permalloy patterns is expected. Although the technology arrives as the utilization of photolithography is pushing to its physical limit, the exploration of electron-beam lithography is just beginning. The empirical as well as scientific knowledge in the production line will certainly lead to larger die size and wafer size. Thus the following contributions to chip complexity improvement are expected in years to come:

Device and circuit cleverness   100 (see below in the section entitled Device Concept Improvement)

Dimension reduction   100 (see below in the section entitled Micro-circuit Fabrication Improvement)

Die size increase   100 (see below in the section entitled Device
                             Concept Improvement)

We shall devote the following sections to presenting the technical rationale for the
above predictions. To foretell our conclusion, we believe that the growing technical
know-how should be able to support or even accelerate the doubling of chip complexity per year in the coming decade and beyond.

Device Concept Improvement

The first-generation bubble products (see above in the section entitled Current
Products) employ T-bar Permalloy patterns to propagate discrete bubbles. The
bubble diameter is d. The memory cell size is A = (4d)^2 = 16d^2 based on 4d bubble
spacing to avoid bubble interaction and insure data integrity. These dimensions are
invariant in discrete bubble devices (in distinction from bubble lattice devices),
even when other ingenious magnetic patterns are utilized to improve device density.
For the T-bar cell, the bar width is d/2 and the gap between the tips of the T
and the bar is only d/3 for effective bubble propagation. Thus the cell size as
expressed in minimum lithography feature W = d/3 becomes A = 16d^2 = 144W^2.
Advanced lithography will make W smaller, but to make smaller the ratio A/W^2 is
the province of "device and circuit cleverness."
There have been several distinct approaches to achieve higher density via
improved device designs:

Gap-tolerant devices   (see Figs. 31a-31d)

Gapless devices   (see Fig. 31e)

Bubble-lattice devices   (see Figs. 31f-31g)

The gap tolerant devices recognize that extra drive field is needed to enable a
bubble to travel across a gap. The gaps are there because discrete spatial points
are needed to accommodate a moving train of magnetic poles. Two groups of structures have been pursued to make bubble propagation more tolerant of the gaps.

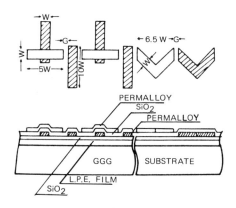

FIG. 31a. Gap-tolerant two-overlay T-bar (after Matsuyama et al. [56]).

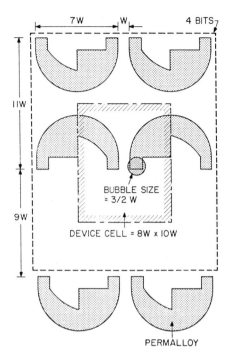

FIG. 31b. Gap-tolerant asymmetrical half-disks (after Bonyhard and Smith [7]).

When the T-bar patterns are decomposed into separate horizontal-line overlay and vertical-line overlay, the overlays can be overlapped to eliminate planar gaps while the interlayer gaps still allow the formation of discrete magnetic poles (see Matsuyama et al. [56]). In such structures, Fig. 31a, the lithography limitation is due to alignment of two overlays rather than the line width itself. The penalty for this approach is two overlays plus alignment instead of one.

The second group of gap tolerant structures are the half disks (see Bonyhard and Smith [7], Bullock et al. [15], and Gergis et al. [57]), chevrons (see Bobeck [58]), and Y-Y patterns (see Yamanouchi et al. [59]). The common feature is to make adjacent Permalloy patterns to have parallel bars at the gap (in contrast to orthogonal bars for the T-bar devices). Thus a bubble is stretched across the gap by two magnetic poles with the same polarity. Moreover, the two airgaps per period

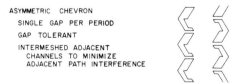

FIG. 31c. Gap-tolerant asymmetrical chevrons (after Bobeck [58], Fig. 4).

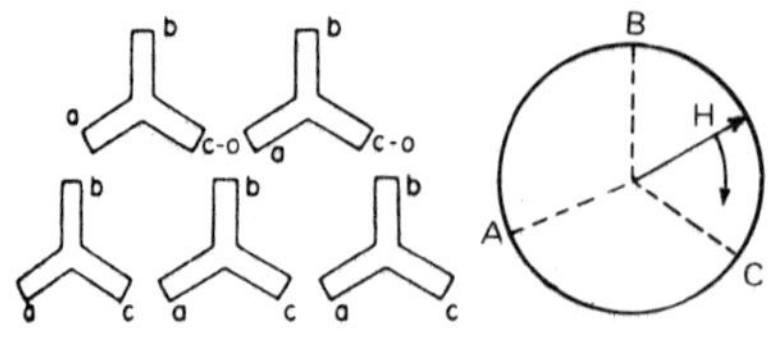

FIG. 31d. Gap-tolerant YY overlay (after Yamanouchi et al. [59]).

in a T-bar device are reduced to a single gap per period. In such structures the gap dimension (minimum lithography feature W) is $d/2$, yielding a cell size of 64 W^2.

The gapless structures are exemplified by the contiguous disk devices (see Wolfe et al. [60] and Lin et al. [61]). The propagation overlay consists of ion-implanted patterns in a thin layer of garnet film. The thin layer is either the surface portion of or an additional deposition on the storage garnet layer. The stress induced by ion implantation forces the magnetization to lie in the film plane. A suitable Permalloy pattern could provide a similar contiguous-disk overlay. The major unique feature is that discrete magnetic poles are created along a narrow domain wall in the overlay and moved by rotating the wall around a crude pattern until it passes the bubble it carries to a similar rotating wall of an adjacent pattern. There are two important consequences of this mode of bubble propagation: First, since the

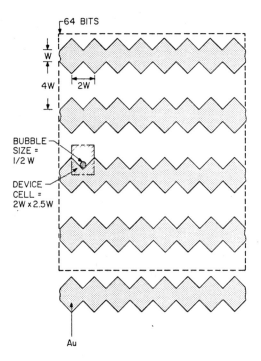

FIG. 31e. Gapless contiguous disks (after Lin et al. [61]).

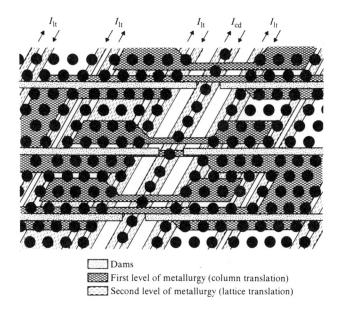

Dams

First level of metallurgy (column translation)

Second level of metallurgy (lattice translation)

FIG. 31f. Conductor-access bubble lattice (after Calhoun et al. [63], Fig. 4).

domain wall width is controlled by the magnetic properties of the overlay [wall width ~ (exchange energy constant/anisotropy constant)$^{\frac{1}{2}}$], the proper choice of material yields wall width of the order of 0.1 μm. By contrast, a lithography shaped pattern would push photolithography to its physical limitation to achieve a 1-μm minimum feature, and it would tax electron-beam lithography to achieve a 0.1-μm minimum feature. The intrinsically small domain walls can manipulate commensurately smaller bubbles. Second, since lithography shaped patterns are used to host the driving walls rather than define minimum features commensurate with the small

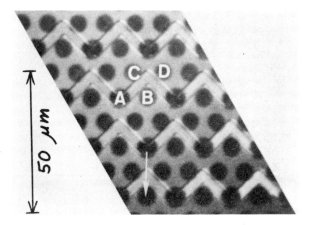

FIG. 31g. Field-access bubble lattice.

bubble size, the patterns can be much larger than the bubbles. For the current design of contiguous-disk devices, the lithography feature is four times that of bubble diameter, thus W = 2d and the cell area is $A = 4W^2$.

The third group of high-density bubble devices are the bubble-lattice devices [62-65]. In contrast to the above two groups, bubble lattice devices compact bubbles into a hexagonal array which is maintained by the mutual repulsion among bubbles. The lattice relies on bubble domain wall configurations to represent information states (ONE and ZERO). Propagation is accomplished by driving directly a fraction of the bubbles in the array (e.g., one out of four) either by conductors [63] or Permalloy patterns [64], but the entire array will propagate due to bubble interactions. Since only a fraction of the bubbles are directly manipulated by lithography shaped patterns, the pattern dimension can be large as compared to individual bubbles. Present designs have W = d/2 to d. Moreover, the closely packed bubbles utilize space more efficiently. Thus each cell is $A = 4d^2$ rather than $16d^2$, resulting in $A = 4W^2$.

Having examined the individual approaches in achieving higher storage density, we shall now further study how they realize the functions necessary to implement complete memory chips. By comparing their different ways in realizing the same functions, we could select the optimum approach to realize each of the needed functions. Moreover, the structures evolved in realizing the various functions suggest optimum combinations of structures to achieve even greater density than anticipated at present in the individual approaches.

Table 12 summarizes methods to realize essential functions for a memory chip in different generic bubble devices. The Permalloy-pattern discrete-bubble devices (generically labeled T-bar) have contributed in conceptual terms to the implementation of several device functions for all three generic devices. They include bubble/void representation of ONE/ZERO, write by the replication or nucleation of a bubble, amplification by stretching a bubble or triggering off the motion of many bubbles, and detection by magnetoresistive effect.

Purely from the viewpoint of improving storage density, several concepts from the various devices seem to enhance rather than exclude one another. Refer to Table 13. By utilizing the fine domain walls to propagate bubbles, the gapless contiguous-disk devices [61, 138] have already achieved $A = 4W^2$ cell area. The double layers [65, 66, 139] as originally proposed respectively for driving and information storage could be extended to three or more layers, all for information storage, while using contiguous-disk overlay for driving. Moreover, the two wall states as employed for information coding in bubble lattice devices [62] could be extended to multiple wall states (e.g., 8 wall states in a bubble to represent three binary bits per bit position). The existence of multiple wall states and their demonstration by different bubble deflection angles from pulsed gradient field direction have been reviewed by Slonczewski and Malozemoff [67]. In conclusion, we envision another order of magnitude reduction in cell size ($A = 0.4W^2$) by the combined approach (see Table 13)—i.e., multilayer multistate gapless devices. Thus we have presented our technical rationale for speculating a more than 350 time improvement in chip complexity by device "cleverness" alone (from $A = 144W^2$ to $A = 0.4W^2$). However, to be on the safe side of the speculation, we have only claimed 10^2 time improvement above in the section entitled Development Forecast for LSI Bubble Devices. A summary of the device density as a function of minimum feature size (lithography capability, see below in the section entitled Microcircuit Fabrication Improvement) and device structure (or device cleverness, this section), with bubble diameter as the parameter (materials, see below in the section entitled Materials Improvement),

TABLE 12
Chip Functions Realized in Various Generic Bubble Devices

Functions	Generic bubble devices		
	T-bar	Contiguous disks	Bubble lattices
Storage	Bubble/void	Bubble/void	(1) Bubble/void Layers: 2 → more (2) Wall states States: 2 → more
Generation		Replication or nucleation	
Amplification	.	Longitudinal stretch Transverse stretch Compressor	
Detection		Magnetoresistive effect	
Bubble motion	Induced field gradient	Charged walls	Induced field gradient
Propagation structure	Permalloy or conductor Gap, gap tolerant, gapless	Ion-implanted overlay Gapless	Permalloy or conductor Gap tolerant
Selection	Transfer line	Transfer line	Access channel
Extra	–	–	Initialization Confinement Buffer Density conversion Wall-state conversion

TABLE 13
Cell Area Reduction through Device Cleverness[a]

Devices	Storage levels/medium layers			
	1/1	3/1	1/3	3/3
Bubbles				
T-bar (W = 0.5d)	$144W^2$	48		
Half-disk (W = d)	64	21		
Bubble lattice (W = d)	4	1.3	1.3	0.4
Contiguous disks (W = 2d)	4	1.3	1.3	0.4
Semiconductors				
MOS	30–$50W^2$			
CD	8–30	3–10		

[a] W = minimum lithography feature. d = bubble diameter.

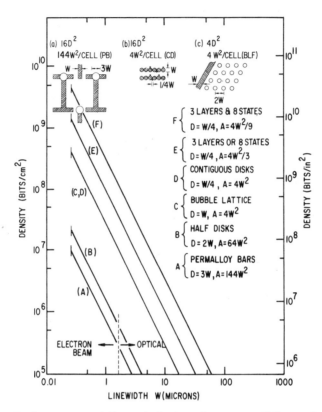

FIG. 32. Density improvement through device cleverness, lithography, and materials. IBM's EL1 system has achieved high-speed production of 22 LSI wafers ($2\frac{1}{4}$ -in.)

is shown in Fig. 32. We shall return to this figure to comment on density improvement strategy below in the section entitled Density and Circuit Complexity Projections.

It is interesting to contrast the anticipated many order of magnitude improvement in bubble devices with the concern over leveling off of improvement in semiconductor devices. A large factor, of course, is the youthful resourcefulness of an emerging new technology. However, bearing in mind that bubbles inspired a totally new semiconductor device approach (namely CCD's), the different principles invoked in bubble device cleverness could and should challenge the semiconductor device designers to rekindle their "cleverness."

Microcircuit Fabrication Improvement

Chang et al. [69] have published a review on where electron-beam (EB) lithography stands. In 1974, Bell Laboratories announced its scanning electron-beam system for mask making, and recently IBM's East Fishkill laboratory has developed a scanning electron-beam system for direct device fabrication in an actual manufacturing environment [70]. Thus EB has indeed become a practical production tool. Bubble devices, due to their simpler structures (down to a single level of critical lithography, see Bobeck et al. [71], are more ready to exploit the electron-beam capability (see Kryder et al. [72]).

Let us first ask: What is the capability of an electron beam vis-à-vis a light beam. When 2-μm device dimensions are produced by photolithography, the mask features are only four wavelengths of visible light in size. Further reduction becomes impractical due to diffraction effects and mechanical damage caused by close proximity. Ultraviolet projection lithographic systems alleviate these difficulties, only to introduce limited depth of focus of their special optics which demands extraordinarily flat wafers. The equivalent wavelength of electrons in the 10 to 28 kV energy range is less than 1Å (10^{-4} μm). However, the ultimate resolution of an electron optical system is limited by aberrations of the electron lenses, the deflection systems, and the electron-electron interactions, rather than by diffraction effects. Lines up to 20 times narrower than the optical limit can be readily generated, resulting in 400X reduction of the area of a cell (or improvement in chip complexity).

Equally important is the use of a computer to control the beam of electrons directly, which facilitates automation and control in mask making and provides rapid turn around time for direct wafer exposure. In addition, an electron beam has a much larger depth of focus than optical systems, and it can readily be used to detect structures on the surface of a sample in the same manner as in the scanning electron microscope. This capability can also be exploited to control the accurate overlay of one pattern on another.

As a production tool, however, electron beam systems are still at the early stage of development. For volume production of extremely dense LSI circuits, progress must be made in several different areas:

High-resolution high-sensitivity electron resists
Systems for forming and deflecting EB
Mechanisms for moving wafer-carrying workstage
Computer generation of circuit patterns
Precision registration of successive layers

The resists suitable for electron exposure must be sensitive (typically 10^{-8} to 10^{-5} C/cm^2), provide high resolution (0.1 to 1 μm minimum line width), and be compatible with IC fabrication processes (including resistance to chemical etching, adhesion to the substrate, temperature stability of the resist image, and resistance to ion-etching methods).

Beam-forming systems use either the Gaussian round-beam approach (based on the probe-forming concept) or the shaped-beam (via square or round apertures) approach. Deflection systems usually employ electromagnetic lenses. Distortions caused by field curvature and isotropic astigmatism of the lens system can be corrected dynamically. As an example, exposures of 0.5 μm lines over a 3×3 mm^2 field can be achieved.

Electron-beam lithographic systems can be grouped into projection systems (to produce patterns by exposure through a mask) and scanning systems (to produce patterns by moving a focused beam). The scanning techniques include raster and vector. In the former the beam scans the entire chip area while switching on and off according to the pattern data. In the latter the beam is scanned only over the paths where writing is required. The electron beam can be stepped at a rate of 100 nsec for each beam location (i.e., 10 MHz). A vector-scan system typically

handles chip sizes 2000 times the minimum pattern line width, but it can also
generate larger sizes by joining adjacent patterns. A 10^6-bit magnetic-bubble test
chip consisting of 2 μm bubbles (<1 μm minimum line width) contained within a
1-cm^2 field has been produced by Texas Instruments.

IBM's EL1 system has achieved high-speed production of 22 $2\frac{1}{4}$-in. LSI wafers
per hour. The throughput for a scanning electron-beam system is determined by
the speed of registration, the table motion, and especially the pattern-writing speed.
For the EL1 producing a 5-mm chip, they are respectively 200, 250, and 960 msec.
The pattern-writing time (T) is given approximately by the number of addresses per
chip (n)/beam stepping rate (f). The beam stepping rate is limited both by the speed
of the deflection system (5 to 20 MHz at present) and by the combined effect of beam
current density (10 to 300 A/cm^2 at present) and resist sensitivity.

In submicron patterns the scanning electron-beam approach is at present the
only proven fabrication technique. The only other technologies that could compete
in the future are electron-beam projection, X-ray (see Spiller and Feder [73], and
shorter-length ultraviolet light conformable masking printing (see Lin [74]). These
techniques could provide higher throughput, but still require that high resolution
masks be produced on the scanning EB system first.

Materials Improvement

Small, stable, and swift bubbles are prerequisite to high-density bubble devices.
The small bubbles are obtained by tailoring the magnetic properties of the storage
medium. This is a major difference of bubbles from semiconductors, in which the
miniaturization is solely controlled by structure making (including lithography) but
no change in the basic material (Si).

At present, all bubble chips in commercial use and advanced development use
liquid-phase-epitaxy garnet films with diameters ranging from 6 to 1 μm. The
smallest bubble diameter is in a contiguous-disk device with ion-implanted garnet-
film overlay (see Lin et al. [61]). A significant experimental material is amorphous
films.

The background for choosing garnet films from many proposed candidates is
reviewed by Chang [9, Chap. 5], and a recent extensive review of bubble memory
materials with comprehensive coverage of the garnet films is made by Nielsen [13].

In spite of the dramatic difference in crystalline states between the single-
crystal epitaxial garnet films and the amorphous GdCoMo alloy films, it appears
that in both materials it is the magnetic parameters which completely determine
the properties of bubbles. The size of the bubble is given by $d = 8(AK)^{\frac{1}{2}}/\pi M^2$, where
A = exchange constant, K = anisotropy constant, and M = magnetization. The stabil-
ity of the bubble requires that $Q = H_k/4\pi M = K/2\pi M^2$ be larger than 1 (where $H_k = 2K/M$ = anisotropy field, $4\pi M$ = demagnetizing field). In fact, practical bubble
devices generally require Q larger than 5. The speed is given by $\nu = \mu \Delta H = (\gamma/16\alpha)(d/Q)$, where γ = gyromagnetic ratio and α = damping constant. The parameter M provides great latitude (a few hundreds to several thousands of Gauss) which
is determined by composition and is under good control. The parameters A (3 to
5×10^{-7} erg/cm) and σ ($\sim 1.76 \times 10^7$ rad/sec Oe) do not allow much variation. The
parameter K is not well understood and is mostly determined empirically. It is
generally believed that both growth-induced and stress-induced anisotropies are
needed to increase K to achieve a usable Q (~ 5).

Garnets are limited in their properties as bubble size is reduced for higher density and, in addition, the garnet wafers are more expensive than Si wafers for semiconductor devices. Therefore, amorphous films have been considered both for lower cost and for improved properties [75]. Both sputtering and evaporation techniques have been developed to produce reliably large unpersonalized amorphous wafers with a wide range of properties at 1/5 the cost of garnet wafers. The properties are comparable and in some cases exceed the available ranges in garnets. However, even though smaller bubbles and higher velocities have been reported, the Q value for stability has not been adequate. In addition, amorphous films have higher conductivity which complicates device structure making. In balance, the amorphous films at present have not superseded the well-established garnet films, but remain a potential candidate for the future [76].

Consequences of Miniaturization

In the preceding pages the technological means for miniaturizing bubble devices have been described. In this section the effects of miniaturization on the electrical characteristics of bubble packages will be assessed. Specifically, the following questions are of interest to us:

A. What is the speed and power trade-off relationship?
B. How does miniturization affect the power dissipation per bit?
C. How does miniaturization affect the current, voltage, and power of on-chip conductors, and the peripheral semiconductor circuits for a bubble memory?
D. How does miniaturization affect data rate?
E. How does miniaturization affect the magnetoresistive sense signal?

Note that these pragmatic questions really amount to what are the ultimate engineering limits of miniaturization. Their complete answers depend on physical laws as well as innovative engineering. The present section attempts to bring together the relevant background information to enable a preliminary assessment.

A Set of Starting Values

Before we consider the consequence of scaling, the electrical characteristics of a commercial bubble module, Texas Instruments' TBM 0103 are summarized in Tables 14 and 15. The module contains a single 92-kbit chip with 5 μm bubble diameter and 10^6 bit/in.^{2} bit density (see Tables 2 and 11).

Scrutinizing Table 14, we observe that the bubble memory module consumes no power in the standby mode and 0.6 W in operation (about 6 μW/bit). The power dissipation in associated circuits is not small, but it takes place in separate semiconductor modules. Also note that only the controller needs standby power while all other circuits do not if the bubble module is switched on only when accessed.

Table 15 makes other interesting revelations. The peak power in the various conductors is not small but the duty cycle is very low. Let us emphasize that for each transfer between the major and minor loops, at least 157 × 2 field rotation periods are needed to generate or sense the data. Thus the duty cycle of the transfer conductor is only (2.5/20)/157 = 0.1%.

TABLE 14
Power Dissipation of a 92-kbit
Magnetic-Bubble Module and Associated Circuits

	Module switched on all the time		Module on only when accessed	
	Standby (W)	Active (W)	Standby (W)	Active (W)
Bubble module	0	0.6	0	0.6
Coil drivers	4.8	5.5	0	1.3
Function drivers	1.6	1.9	0	0.5
Sense amplifier	0.7	0.7	0	0.18
Function timing	0.3	0.3	0	0.3
Controller	1.0	1.0	1.0[a]	1.0
Miscellaneous logic	1.5	1.5	0	1.5
Total	9.9	11.5	1.0	5.38

[a]Can also be switched.

On a per bit basis, the generator consumes more power (0.16 W/bit) and more frequently (potentially once per cycle). The duty cycle in the generate conductor is $0.3/20 = 1.5\%$.

As we shall see below in the section entitled Intrinsic Limits and Tradeoffs, the power dissipation associated with bubble motion is extremely small. Thus the order of importance in determining power dissipation and speed of a bubble module is:

On-chip conductor
Coils
Bubble film and overlay

The last item is perhaps negligible. Nevertheless, the control of the magnetic parameters of the bubble film is the key to miniaturization, and magnetization

TABLE 15
Current Rating and Power Dissipation
in Conductors on the TBM 0103 Chip

	Nominal current (mA)	Duration (μsec)	Resistance (Ω)	Peak power (W)
Generate	250	0.3	2.5	0.16
Replicate	120	1.56	5.5	0.079
Annihilate	60	4.7	5.5	0.02
Transfer-in	46	1.7	317	0.6
Transfer-out	27	2.5	317	0.21
Detector	5.5	dc	1000	0.03
Rotating field	800			0.5
Cycle time		20		

value is the determining factor of currents and power. It is also obvious that it is the conductor layout, coil layout, and operation modes which must receive innovative design attention if the current and power increases attendant to miniaturization are to be circumvented.

Scaling with Bubble Diameter (and Magnetization)

Bubble device miniaturization begins with reducing bubble size. Thiele [77] has analyzed the bubble diameter dependence on materials parameters (magnetization, anisotropy, exchange constant), geometrical parameter (film thickness), and bias field. Some of Thiele's results relevant to our discussion here are:

Bubble radius and circuit period $\sim 1/M_s^2$

Bit density $\qquad\qquad\qquad\qquad \sim M_s^4 \sim 1/d^2$

Bubble field $\qquad\qquad\qquad\qquad \sim M_s \sim 1/d^{\frac{1}{2}}$

where M_s is the saturation magnetization of the storage medium.

It is intuitively clear that in order for the magnetic overlay (with magnetization M_o, thickness t_o, and width W_o) to influence the motion of bubbles (with magnetization M_b and diameter d_b), the total magnetic flux supplied by an overlay pattern ($M_o t_o W_o$) is equal to that of a bubble ($\pi M_b d_b^2/4$). Thus

$$M_o t_o W_o \sim M_b d_b^2$$

$$M_o t_o / W_o \sim M_b d_b^2 / W_o^2 \sim M_b$$

that is, the demagnetizing field in the overlay is proportional to the bubble magnetization value. For the tiny patterns the drive field is entirely used to overcome the demagnetizing field; hence the planar drive field is equal to the demagnetizing field, which in turn is proportional to the bubble magnetization. Thus we have deduced another relationship useful for scaling:

Drive field $(H_{xy}) \sim M_s \sim 1/d^{\frac{1}{2}}$

For readers more mathematically inclined, the papers by George et al. [78, 79] and Almasi and Lin [80] could be consulted. These papers generalize the stability treatment of Thiele to include the presence of a Permalloy pattern. However, the readers should expect to be contented with lengthy numerical solutions but not a single-line equation for dimensional analysis purposes.

Consequences

The total power dissipated in a rotating-field coil is given by

$$P_T \propto a^2 H^2 \phi(f)$$

where $\quad$ a = edge length of coil
$\qquad\qquad$ H = rotating field
$\qquad\quad \phi(f)$ = a function to account for proximity effect
$\qquad\qquad\qquad \sim f^{\frac{1}{2}}$ for single layer coils
$\qquad\qquad$ f = rotating field frequency

The answer to Question A is revealed by the above formula; namely, the power dissipation increases rapidly with frequency (i.e., data rate). Saito et al. [25] have discussed how this power can be limited. For a coil pair with volume $2.5 \times 4.8 \times 0.5$ cm^3 to supply 40 Oe rotating field to 2 Mbits on 32 chips each of 64 bits, 2.5 W is dissipated at 20 kHz, 5 W at 100 kHz, and 22 W at 500 kHz. Since the power dissipation is mainly due to skin-effect loss, the solid wire can be replaced by a bundle of interlaced thin insulated wires (litz wire) to reduce the loss. When the above coils use litz wires, the power dissipation is only 4 W between 20 and 200 kHz, and only increases to 8 W at 500 kHz (4 μW/bit for a 6-μm bubble at 24 μm spacing). As to conductor power dissipation, the increased data rate does not raise peak power but will increase duty cycle.

To answer Question B, let us do a scaling exercise on power dissipation. Given the same number of chips and number of bits per chip,

$$\text{coil dimension} \sim \text{bubble radius} \sim 1/M_s^2$$

$$\text{field} \sim M_s$$

hence

$$\text{total power dissipation} \sim a^2 H^2 \sim \left(\frac{1}{M_s^2}\right)^2 M_s^2 \sim \frac{1}{M_s^2} \sim d$$

In other words, the total power dissipation and the power dissipation per bit will decrease with the bubble diameter. In fact, for gapless devices in which the drive field increases less rapidly than M_S, the power dissipation will decrease faster than the bubble diameter. However, we should also note that with miniaturization, the total power dissipation scales down with d, but the total coil surface area available for dissipating heat scales down with d^2. Thus, while the power dissipation per bit is decreased, the heat dissipation per unit surface area is increased. Given the fact that the bubble storage medium is temperature sensitive, improved heat dissipation for the coils is imperative.

The current, voltage, power, and current density for the on-chip conductors are given respectively by

$$I = Hw$$

$$V = IR = Hw \cdot \rho \ell / wt = H\ell(\rho/t)$$

$$I^2R = (Hw)^2 \rho \ell / wt = H^2 w\ell(\rho/t)$$

$$I/wt = Hw/wt = H/t$$

With miniaturization,

$$H \sim M$$

$$w, \quad \ell \sim 1/M^2 \sim d$$

$$t = \text{conductor thickness (kept constant)}$$

$$\rho = \text{resistivity} = \text{constant}$$

hence

$$I \sim 1/M \sim d^{\frac{1}{2}}$$

$$V \sim M/M^2 \sim 1/M \sim d^{\frac{1}{2}}$$

$$I^2R \sim M^2(1/M^2)^2 \sim 1/M^2 \sim d$$

$$I/wt \sim M \sim 1/d^{\frac{1}{2}}$$

Now to answer Question C, we see that current, voltage, and power dissipation all decrease with miniaturization, but the current density increases even though the conductor thickness is maintained constant.

Since both for the coils and the on-chip conductors the power dissipation decreases with miniaturization ($\sim d$), this decrease can be used to compensate for the increase in power dissipation associated with higher data rate. Thus we have answered Question D.

To answer Question E, let us examine the sense signal expression:

$$V_s = i_s \Delta R_s$$

$$= i_s (\Delta \rho_s) \ell/wt$$

When the thickness of the magnetoresistor is maintained constant while the width is decreased, the demagnetizing field will increase:

$$H_d \sim t/w \sim 1/d$$

The field from the bubble also increases, but at a slower rate:

$$H_{bubble} \sim M_s \sim 1/d^{\frac{1}{2}}$$

Thus $\Delta \rho_s$ will decrease with miniaturization. If the magnetoresistor thickness is also scaled as d, then H_d will remain the same, but $\Delta \rho_s$ will increase with miniaturization due to increased H_{bubble}. If the length is decreased, the sense signal can be maintained only when the sense current is increased. Since i_s is small and Permalloy can sustain higher current density, larger i_s is a feasible approach within certain limits.

Intrinsic Limits and Tradeoffs

While the practical implementations are dictated by coil and circuit designs, it is of interest to consider the intrinsic limits which the engineering designs could aspire to but never reach. Keyes [81] has presented an heuristic analysis in that vein.

He defines two basic parameters: characteristic length (L) and characteristic energy (U). The characteristic length is related to the wall energy σ and the saturation magnetization M_s:

$$L = \sigma/4\pi M_s^2$$

where $\sigma = 4(AK_u)^{\frac{1}{2}}$

A = exchange constant

K_u = crystalline anisotropy constant

Since $K_u > 2\pi M_s^2$ in order to sustain magnetization normal to the film, $L^2 > 4A/K_u$. The film thickness that allows the smallest bubble is $h = 4L$, and the diameter of the minimal bubble in the center of its range of stability is $8L$.

The characteristic material energy is defined as

$$U = \sigma^3/(4\pi M_s^2)^2 = \sigma L^2$$

Since $K_u > 2\pi M_s^2$, $U > 8AL$. The binding energy of a bubble, that is, the energy barrier that it would have to overcome in order to collapse, is about $10U$. The binding energy of a bubble to a preferred site (e.g., a Permalloy pattern) is a few U, so that the energy that must be expended to release a bubble from its site and move is a few U.

The inertial effects of domain wall motion play a significant part in bubble energetics at a velocity V given by

$$V = (4\pi M_s)\pi\gamma A/\sigma = (4\pi L/U)^{\frac{1}{2}}\pi\gamma A$$

where γ = gyromagnetic ratio; numerically $\gamma^2 = 0.8 \times 10^{14}$ cm/g. Since the kinetic energy of the bubble becomes comparable to the other contributions to its energy at this velocity V, the stability, shape, and size of the bubble are significantly altered, and it is reasonable to regard V as the maximum velocity at which a bubble may be moved.

The minimum time required to move a bubble from one preferred site to another may be written as

$$T = 4 \times 8L/V = 32L/V$$

Thus the shortest per-bit propagation time is

$$T = 32(UL/4\pi)^{\frac{1}{2}}/\pi\gamma A$$

The power per bit could be defined as $4U/T$:

$$P = (4\pi U/L)^{\frac{1}{2}}\pi\gamma A/8$$

Let us assign practical values to the materials parameters.

$A \sim 10^{-6}$ erg/cm

$\gamma^2 = 0.8 \times 10^{14}$ cm/g

$K_u > 10^7$ erg/cm^3

the values of L, U, V, T and P are found to be

$L > 6 \times 10^{-7}$ cm $= 60$ Å

$U \sim 10^{-8}$ erg

$v < 3.5 \times 10^4$ cm/sec

$T \sim 6$ nsec

$P > 0.04$ erg/sec $= 0.004$ μW

Indeed the bubbles may be very small, its energy much smaller than the 10^{-3} to 10^{-4} erg required by the most modern transistor logic, and the power substantially smaller than the basic power level of semiconductor logic devices.

Other interesting papers by Keyes on intrinsic limits include one on micro-structure fabrication [82] and one on uncertainty and information [83].

Memory Module Cost Breakdown

Cost information on commercial products is difficult to obtain, partly due to the variability of production conditions but mainly due to the manufacturer's reluc-tance to reveal production data. Yet it is of importance to know the cost estimate as a measure of viability against competing technologies, and to know the cost break-down since it reveals the proper areas for further technical efforts to reduce cost. Takasu et al. [84] presented a design for an 8×10^6 bit bubble memory along with a cost breakdown based on their engineering model. Since the results appear reason-able, we shall repeat their report here in order to extrapolate the general trend for future cost-effective product developments.

The memory consists of 8 10^6-bit memory boards and 2 control boards. Each memory board contains four packages, each in turn containing four 80-kbit chips sharing drive coils, magnets, and shielding. Each board is also provided with drivers, a decoder, and a 16-input sense amplifier, as well as a 1-kbit PROM to select 128 nondefective loops out of 136 minor loops.

The cost estimates for the memory system are shown in Fig. 33. The chip cost is treated as a variable since it still involves unknown factors (such as yield). If the chip cost is assumed to be $15, the system cost becomes less than 0.05¢/bit, an attractive cost for a nonvolatile millisecond-access memory. It is noteworthy that even for a small memory of 8×10^6 bits, the chips account for almost half of the cost per bit. When larger-capacity memories are to be constructed, the chips are going to be the dominant cost factor. Indeed, the current pursuit for high-density simple-processing devices (see above in the sections entitled Device Concept Im-provement, Microcircuit Fabrication Improvement, and Materials Improvement) is aimed at reducing the chip cost on a per bit basis.

The circuitry accounts for one-quarter of the cost per bit. The cost of PROM is only 3% of the system cost. This means that the cost incurred in adding PROM's is small as compared with the cost reduction effected by chip yield increase. The

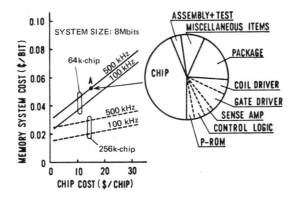

FIG. 33. Cost breakdown for an 8-Mbit memory system. (After Takasu et al. [84], Fig. 7.)

control logic also contributes to only a small percentage of the cost per bit. It is inferred that adding logic circuits will enhance data management and manipulation capabilities without undue cost increase.

Package contributes to about 20% of the cost per bit. It should be emphasized that the package cost is quite sensitive to field amplitude and frequency. Both the coil driver's power and the package's ability to dissipate heat are limited. At higher drive field (as incurred with smaller bubbles) or higher frequency, the number of chips per package must be reduced, thus contributing to a significant increase in cost per bit. See Fig. 9 of Takasu et al [84].

The current approach to bubble packaging is a cumbersome one; essentially, it attempts to package a large chip or multiple chips to share the package and the drivers. However, this entails driving all the bits in the package, whether needed or not, thus dissipating power unnecessarily. With the trend toward even larger chip (more bits) and smaller bits (higher drive field), more modular arrangement (e.g., striplines instead of coils) and selective drive (e.g., coincident selection) will be needed for both power and cost reduction.

Market Projection

Bubbles are of a wide range of applications, as has already been revealed by memory modules for microprocessors at the low end and space-flight recorders at the high end. With the projected steady increase in chip complexity (a factor of 2 improvement per year for the next 15 years, see the sections entitled Development Forecast for LSI Bubble Devices and Density and Circuit Complexity Projections) and the versatile functional capability (see the sections entitled Versatility of Shift Registers and Major/Minor Loops; Subsystems, Architectures, and Programming; and Performance), bubble applications can be expected to grow continuously. It is of interest to have an overview of the potential market for bubbles. The important question to bear in mind is whether the market is big enough to support the continual development of this new technology.

A survey of the "disk" storage demand in 1974 (established) and in 1980 (projected) by Wickham [85] is summarized in Table 16. The system types refer to different applications areas such as large electronic data processing center (large EDP) and minicomputer-based systems. The term "disk" refers to actual storage hardware in use in 1974, but is used as a generic term referring to storage devices with current or improved disk characteristics in 1980. Although projections of the type shown in Table 16 are not free of risk and uncertainty, we may nevertheless draw some tentative conclusions. It appears that large and medium systems dominate the bit volume both at present and in the future. Especially for medium EDP, both the total bit volume and the growth factor are high. Due to the large capacity per system, cost competitiveness with the current disk files appears to be a prerequisite for a new technology to qualify for this market. A rule of thumb is that solid-state devices must achieve at least 10 times higher density than disk files in order to be cost competitive. The storage density for disk files is 10^6 bits/in.^{2} (IBM 3340 disk file) at present and is still improving. Considerable improvement in bubble density is required before it can win a place in the large and medium EDP storage market. However, even though the estimate of 10^4 time improvement in density (see page 51) may sound outrageous, when spread out as a factor of 2 incremental improvement per year over the next 15 years it becomes a more reasonable aspiration.

TABLE 16
Summary of "Disk" Storage Demand in the United States

System type	Byte/system	1974 ($\times 10^9$ byte)	1980 ($\times 10^9$ byte)	Growth factor
Large EDP	2.4×10^9	1200	2640	2.2
Medium EDP	0.6×10^9	720	5520	7.7
Small EDP	10^7	70	300	4.3
Mini	2.5×10^6	75	450	6.0
Micro	–	–	8	–
Processing terminal	3×10^6	42	210	5.0
Intelligent terminal	10^6	25	285	11.4
Simple terminal	–	–	–	–
Total		2132	9413	4.4

By contrast, for a mature disk-file technology, further improvement becomes more difficult, particularly when one realizes that the state of the art is already pushing the separation between head and disk surface to several thousand Angstroms, a distance to be maintained when the head moves with respect to the disk at 70 m/sec.

The applications which can use smaller storage units are a different matter. They are relatively new and diverse. The devices in use today are fixed-head disk files, floppy disks, tape cassettes, and cartridges. The total bit volume is much less than that for the large and medium EDP applications, but the projected growth is large. Since "processing capability" and "intelligence" are emphasized for such applications, capabilities in addition to storage are expected. In the section above entitled Versatility of Shift Registers and Major/Minor Loops, some unconventional capabilities in conventional shift-register and major/minor loop chips have already been enumerated. Additional functional capabilities such as addressing, associative search, sorting, text editing, and data base manipulation will be described below in the section entitled Subsystems, Architectures, and Programming. Thus competitive cost, modularity, nonvolatility, and functional capability are the attractive features of bubbles for small system applications. However, CCD's and FET's are also strong contenders in the area of small-storage applications, particularly when nonvolatility is not essential and speed is essential.

Density and Circuit Complexity Projections

This section will bring together the threads of thought presented in the preceding subsections of Forecast for LSI Bubbles.

Cost reduction and market volume are mutually dependent. They are quantitatively related by the learning curve; i.e., the present cost per bit will be reduced by 30% when the present cumulative volume is doubled. The eventual market volume for bubbles is suggested by the estimated demand for disk-like storage: 10^{14} bits/year beyond 1980 (Table 16). This large volume is expected to support the research and development expenditure and sustain the cost reduction along the learning curve. The various ways to achieve high density and large chip are the technical means to obtain low cost per bit. The high performance and functional capability of bubbles will make them more attractive than disks when they become cost competitive.

The dominant factor in bubble storage system hardware cost is the bubble chip. The main avenue to achieve low-cost chips is to obtain high device density and large chip bit capacity (see above in the section entitled Memory Module Cost Breakdown).

Historically speaking, semiconductor IC chips have sustained an annual increase of 2 in chip bit capacity for the last 15 years. One could make two inferences. First, the various technologies required for LSI are capable of supporting this pace of progress. Second, the customers expect this pace of progress (see above in the section entitled Historical Trends of LSI Semiconductor Devices).

The factors responsible for semiconductor LSI growth will also be the factors responsible for bubble LSI growth: device cleverness (see above in the section entitled Device Concept Improvement), lithography (see above in the section entitled Microcircuit Fabrication Improvement), and experience gained through expanding usage (learning curve). Moreover, at present there appears to be much more room for device improvement for bubbles than for semiconductors (see above in the section entitled Device Concept Improvement). We anticipate a 10^4 time increase in device density and a comparable increase in chip bit capacity in the next two decades (see above in the section entitled Development Forecast for LSI Bubble Devices). Very likely, this progress will be spread out as a sustained improvement of a factor of 2 per year.

There are a number of alternatives in achieving steadily improving densities. In the section above entitled Device Concept Improvement, we have emphasized that the several approaches (see Fig. 31) currently being pursued are not mutually exclusive (see Tables 12 and 13, and Fig. 32). They include: gap-tolerant devices which include single-level-masking designs to better explore high-resolution electron-beam lithographies, gapless devices such as contiguous-disk devices to manipulate small bubbles with crude patterns, and bubble lattices to enable closer packing of bits. Moreover, we speculated that multilayer and multistate devices will emerge in the future.

In Fig. 32 the device density is plotted as a function of lithography for the various types of device designs. The curves are not only crowded but sometimes overlapping. However, the theme of alternative routes to density improvement and their technology requirements perhaps are better illustrated by placing these curves together.

1. See Curve a. The T-bar devices ($144W^2$) are the basic elements of all the first generation bubble products. The 2-μm minimum feature is already at the limit of the state-of-the-art photolithography capability. Any further significant improvement in device density must be derived from the use of electron-beam lithography. Then a 10^2 time ultimate improvement in density could be expected, assuming a 0.2 μm minimum feature.

2. See Curve b. The half-disk devices, which have enabled the realization of 10^6-bit chips [14], double the density of T-bar devices at the same minimum feature. They also make unit cell area for bubble devices ($64W^2$) approach that of semiconductor devices ($30W^2$). However, sustained significant improvement in device density still cannot be obtained without electron-beam lithography.

3. See Curve c. This curve should be considered to be a representative curve in a region comprised of both a variety of contiguous-disk designs and a variety of bubble-lattice designs. The contiguous-disk devices [61] are a generic class of devices with no airgaps in the propagation structure and with propagation-pattern minimum feature larger than bubble diameter. However, just as in T-bar and half-disk devices, the discrete adjacent bubbles must be separated

by 4 bubble diameters. The cell size is fixed in terms of D ($16D^2$), but somewhat variable in terms of W (e.g., 2 to $4W^2$).

The bubble lattice devices (see Figs. 31f and 31g) are another generic class of devices which maintain stable storage array by the mutual repulsion of closely spaced bubbles. They include conductor-access (see Calhoun et al. [63]), field access (see Ho and Chang [64]), and automation type (see Argyle et al. [86]), or their combinations. Although stable hexagonal-closely-packed bubbles in the absence of bias field average $1.5D^2$ per cell under static conditions, practical devices allow greater spacing between bubbles to facilitate their movement (e.g., $4D^2$). Again, the cell size is relatively fixed in terms of D ($4D^2$), but more variable in terms of W (e.g., from 4 to $16W^2$), depending on minimum feature size which is affected by the number of bubbles per pattern.

Given the same lithography capability, both contiguous-disk devices and bubble-lattice devices offer more than 10 times density than gap-tolerant devices (T-bar and half-disks). Even within photolithography limits, one could hope to achieve close to 10^8 bits/in.^{2} density. Bubble-lattice devices are less limited by the difficulty of obtaining small bubble materials (D = W instead of D = W/2). On the other hand, the contiguous-disk devices are less encumbered by the requirement of wall state conversion and density conversion.

4. See Curve d. Again this curve represents one of two alternatives: a three storage-layer device or an eight storage-level device. The basic device could be of the contiguous-disk type (noninteracting laterally, i.e., within the same layer), or of the bubble-lattice file (bubbles interacting within a layer). However, domain wall states are used to represent information states in both types.

   In the multilayer device (e.g., three layers), bubbles are coupled magneto-statically from layer to layer in a vertical column. In the multistate device, only one layer of storage medium is assumed, but each bubble may assume one of eight possible domain-wall states, thus representing 3 bits per site instead of 1. The per-bit cell area is $4W^2/3$ or (4 to $16D^2$)/3. Note that the circuitry to sort out bits from multilayers or multistates is yet to be devised.

5. See Curve e. Multilayers and multistates could be used simultaneously for the storage cells (see Fig. 34), thus reducing the per-bit cell area to $4W^2/9$ or (4 to $16D^2$)/9.

   This could push the device density to 3×10^8 bits/in.^{2} with 2 μm photolithography and 2×10^{10} bits/in.^{2} with 0.2 μm electron-beam lithography. Moreover, in this aggressive device structure, even with 5 μm bubbles and 10 μm lines, better than 10^7 bits/in.^{2} device density could be obtained (a factor of 10 higher than that of current bubble products).

6. It is noteworthy that the full pursuit of device cleverness without resorting to electron-beam lithography could yield 300 times density improvement over the present products. Paced at a factor of 2 improvement per year, this could fuel the progress for the next 8 years. This may well be a preferred approach since it avoids the expenditure of electron-beam apparatus, the yet unfamiliar small-bubble materials, the electromigration problem in microconductors, and a host of other problems associated with microstructure making.

Let us next consider how to improve the bit capacity per chip. The usual avenues to larger chip capacity are higher device density and experience which is quantitatively expressed as the learning curve. There is a particular bubble memory organization scheme—coincident selection (see below in the section entitled Coincident Selection)—

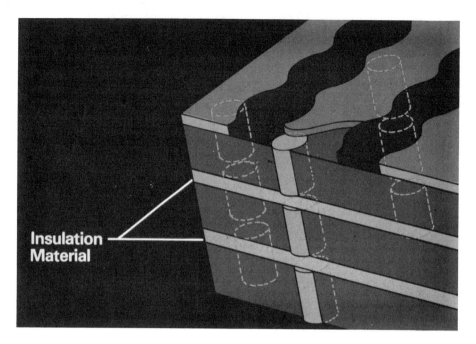

FIG. 34. An example of multilayer multistate bubble devices.

that appears to offer the opportunity to add to chip complexity by an order of magnitude or more without suffering the initial loss of yield (i.e., no need for a long period of "learning curve" experience). The scheme uses fault-tolerant wide conductors to interconnect a matrix of storage arrays to share chip pads and supporting circuits. If the array size is chosen to be the one offering minimum cost per function (see Fig. 27b), and many such arrays are connected according to the coincident-selection scheme, the same yield (hence same low cost per bit) will be maintained for the larger chip of many arrays.

The number of interconnectable arrays is finite. However, 9 to 16 arrays can be reasonably assumed to yield an order of magnitude increase in chip bit capacity.

Competition with CCD's

The charge-coupled devices have the simplest structures, are the easiest to process, and potentially offer the lowest cost per bit among all semiconductor read-and-write memory devices. As such, they present the most direct competition to bubble memories. CCD memory chips are available from several semiconductor manufacturers. INTEL has announced a CCD memory system which contains 16 memory units, 1 control unit, and 1 buffer unit, with a total storage capacity of 1.88×10^7 bits (see Electronics 48(17), 109 (1975)). The data rate is 2 MHz, the access time 0.2 msec, and the system cost 0.2¢/bit (bound to decrease).

Another interesting development is the announced intention of Burroughs Corp. to introduce the Burroughs Scientific Processor, a large-scale system "suited to

the largest problem-solving requirements of science, industry, and government"
(see Computer World, Burroughs unveils supercomputer with array design, April 11,
1977, p. 39). At the heart of the system are the CCD devices for "file memory"
with a capacity expandable from 4 to 67 million 56-bit words (i.e., up to 3.75×10^9
bits). The fast file memory holds programs and data for use by a control processor
and parallel processors, and offers an access time of 500 μsec and a transfer rate
of 75×10^6 bytes/sec. The multiple processors in parallel are capable of handling
50×10^6 operations/sec, and suitable for solving large vector-oriented problems.
The purchase price ranges from 3.8 to 6.1 million dollars (i.e., up to 0.2¢/bit
when averaged over 3.75×10^9 bits).

The central issues in comparing bubbles and CCD's are three: potential cost
reduction, nonvolatility, and speed. As we are projecting into the future (beyond 10
years), the aggressive designs should be considered. Both CCD cells and bubble
memory cells (contiguous disks or bubble lattice) occupy an area of $4W^2$ per cell
where W is the minimum line width in the cell design. Given the same lithography
capability, they could be made with comparable density. However, bubbles are
probably more amenable to fewer levels of lithography due to simpler device structure. Multiple storage levels have been proposed for both CCD's and bubbles. For
example, eight levels of charge would enable each CCD cell to represent 3 bits of
information instead of 1. (Four-level, or 2 bit/site, devices have already been fabricated [87]. Eight domain-wall states would enable each bubble to store 3 bits.
Since an overlay may extend its influence over more than one storage layer, multilayer bubble media sharing a common overlay are possible, thus further enhancing
density. We believe bubbles may offer a factor of 10 density advantage over CCD's,
assuming the same degree of fabrication sophistication.

Reliable data storage certainly cannot tolerate volatility, particularly when a
large capacity memory is not backed up by a nonvolatile disk file. The use of bat-
teries to guard against power failure in volatile but low-power memories may be
a reasonable approach. However, a numerical example will shed more light
on the problem. The INTEL 128 kbyte card consumes 46 W in operation (i.e.,
48 μW/bit), and 7.5 W in standby mode (i.e., 7.5 μW/bit). Bit density improvement
will bring the standby power to below 5 W, thus within the capability of a 12 V
10 A-hr battery for 24 hr. Such a battery takes up 120 in.^{3}, weighs 11 lb, and requires support electronics (voltage regulation, charging, transition circuitry, memory failure detection, etc.) costing tens of dollars. One could estimate the added
cost per bit on the order of 5 to 10 m¢ from the battery and its accessories.

The charge transfer rate of CCD's is about 100 MHz. However, the chip
operation is limited by the power dissipation in the peripheral circuits to a frequency on the order of 2 to 10 MHz. The bubble devices will improve their data
rate from the present 0.1 MHz to above 1 MHz but will remain slower than CCD's
since domain wall motion is a slower physical process than charge transfer. As to
access speed, both devices can benefit from similar memory array organization
techniques. In fact, the familiar long shift registers, major-minor loops, and
decoders in bubbles [88] have their counterparts [89] in CCD's as serpentine shift
register, serial-parallel-serial shift register, and line-addressable random-access
memory, respectively [90].

CCD's are being actively pursued and extensively reported. A recently published volume of reprint papers, edited by Melen and Buss [91], provides a general
survey of the subject.

Competition with Disks

It is an unfortunate fact of life that as a technology becomes more successful in the market, detailed technical information becomes less available. Magnetic disk technology is one such example. Nevertheless, we may cite the following references as the background information. IBM Journal of Research and Development (18(6), (November 1974)) is devoted to magnetic recording technologies, surveying state of the art in areas of bearing and aerodynamics, servos, head and media technologies, signal processing, etc. Harker and Chang [92] and Haughton [93] presented overviews of disk storage systems. Gagliardi [94] discussed the influence of mechanical disks on the architecture of data management systems, and Rasmussen [95] on the restrictions to applications growth due to limitations in disk characteristics.

Disks offer a wide range of storage applications: from fixed head files (tens of msec access time) to moving head files (hundreds of msec access time); from floppy disks (10^6 bits) to disk drives (10^{10} bits); from removable flexible media to removable disk packs to fixed media. In terms of intrinsic capabilities and long-term potentials (in contrast to current realities), bubbles cover the full range of disk capabilities. The central issues in the bubbles vs disks competition are then, in each category of applications, how soon bubbles could become a viable competitor, and what functional advantages bubbles have to offer to supersede disks.

The storage density for disk files is 10^6 bits/in.^{2} (IBM 3340) at present. In the early days of the disk technology, 1955 to 1965, the density was improved from 2×10^3 to 2×10^5 bits/in.^{2}. In more recent years, 1965 to 1975, the improvement (2×10^5 to 10^6 bits/in.^{2}) has slowed down (see Fig. 2 of Harker and Chang [92]). One may ask whether the improvement is approaching some intrinsic physical limits. The areal density of disks is determined by storage medium thickness, airgap in the read/write heads, and the separation between head and media. These three geometrical parameters are about equal. One may state more specifically that the bit dimension is proportional to the head-medium separation. At present, the head-to-medium separation is already below 1 μm. Further reduction would be much more difficult, particularly keeping in mind that this separation must be kept constant while the head is moving at 50 m/sec with respect to the disk surface. Thus even very aggressive prediction does not place further improvement in disk density beyond 10^8 bits/in.^{2}. At present the bubble products are at 10^6 bits/in.^{2} density, advanced research prototype chips at 10^8 bits/in.^{2}, and optimistic predictions (see above in the section entitled Density and Circuit Complexity Projections) at 10^{10} bits/in.^{2}.

The general nature of competition between bubbles and a number of other technologies is very well reflected in Fig. 35, although the numerical data may evoke partisan debates. Let us make several observations: (1) Solid-state devices (bubbles and semiconductors) are much more modular than mechanical devices (disks and tapes). The former entered the market with a capacity as small as 1 kbit chips at a price below $100, while the latter, with capacities ranging from 10^6 bits (floppy disks) through 10^8 bits (head-per-track disks) to 10^8 to 10^{10} bits (moving-head disks), with prices between several hundred dollars and hundreds of thousands of dollars. This is due to the fact that the mechanical drive, servo, electronics, etc. are expensive and must be amortized over large capacity. (2) Integrated circuit economics are such that low cost can be maintained for larger capacity modules if the larger capacity is accomplished by higher density. Thus we note the micron-size lithography bubble devices priced from a

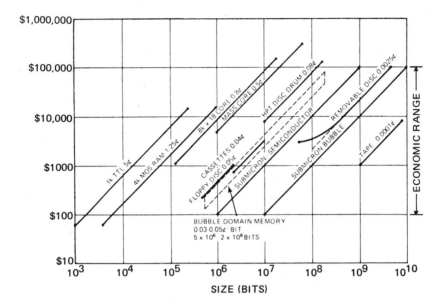

FIG. 35. Inherent economics of mass memories. Disk files reduce cost per bit by placing more bit volume per drive. LSI technologies reduce cost per bit by pushing for higher storage density. (After EDN [97], Fig. 2.)

few hundred dollars and up offer 5×10^6 to 2×10^8 bits (at 0.05¢/bit). The submicron-size electron-beam lithography bubble devices (alternatively micron-size photo-lithography bubble devices, but augmented with multilayers or multistates, see above in the section entitled Density and Circuit Complexity Projections), still priced from a few hundred dollars and up, offer more than ten times higher capacity (at more than ten times reduction in cost-per-bit). (3) If the data in Fig. 35 are accepted as a valid framework, one could anticipate bubbles becoming competitive with both floppy disks (the complete system, not just the media) and head-per-track disks in a few years, and with moving-head disks in about a decade.

Some readers may feel uncomfortable with the lack of detailed technical sub-stantiation of the data in Fig. 35. They may consult Harker and Chang [92] on disks and Sutherland et al. [96] on integrated circuits for discussions of the relevant technological factors to be evaluated.

The second central issue is the functional advantages of bubbles vis-à-vis disks. This issue is discussed at length in the sections entitled Current Products; Versa-tility of Shift Registers and Major/Minor Loops; Subsystems, Architectures, and Programming; and Performance. While these sections emphasize how bubbles can be used differently from and advantageously over disks, we should bear in mind that the software in existing computing systems, which is extensive and expensive, has been built around the desk devices. This may constrain bubbles to be used to simulate disks, when they become cost competitive. However, in small systems and new applications, many of the innovative approaches for bubbles are most likely to be attempted.

SUBSYSTEMS, ARCHITECTURES, AND PROGRAMMING

Subsystems are the building blocks for computer systems. Computer architecture is the discipline of organizing and interconnecting memory and logic elements into subsystems and then subsystems into a computer system. A program is a sequence of instructions that are understood and executed by a computer to perform tasks. We are interested in placing bubble technology in the proper perspective of subsystems, architectures, and programs. After all, these are the disciplines users are interfaced with, rather than domain walls and Permalloy patterns.

The level of integration on commercially available chips of solid-state devices reached 10^5 components in 1977. By maintaining the current rate of progress, 10^6-component chips will be on the market within 4 years, and 10^8-component chips will materialize within 10 years. Significant design changes will be induced by the chip technology advances. First of all, while the chip capacity will grow exponentially, the number of interconnections available for I/O will not increase significantly. To avoid traffic congestion, each chip will be forced to be more self-sufficient. This necessitates logic capability on the memory chips. Second, while hardware cost will continue to decrease dramatically as a consequence of increased chip complexity (i.e., density increase plus chip capacity increase), it does not appear that software will become less expensive. Thus there will be a greater reliance on hardware to provide desired functions. Third, chip-based technologies are more amenable to distributed processing and distributed data base vis-à-vis a powerful central processor unit standing side by side with a huge storage concentrated on mechanical disk files. Multiple chips are more amenable to parallel processing as well as to specialization of functions on different chips.

In view of the above trends, the design of future computers will have greater integration, thus transcending the traditional demarcation lines of subsystems, architectures, and programs. An exposure to these individual views will help efforts toward integrated designs. In this section we try to bring together the views on bubble memories as expressed by the subsystem designers, architects, and programmers.

Views of Subsystem Designers

In Table 17 the variety of components for bubble memory subsystems is listed. While all these components are conceptually valid, only very few of them have been fabricated and tested. The devices in use include simple long shift registers and simple major/minor loops (see above in the section entitled Current Products). More versatile versions of these devices, considered very likely to materialize in the near future, were described above in the section entitled Versatility of Shift Registers and Major/Minor Loops. This section will discuss the remaining components listed in Table 17 for which there has been very limited experimental work done, and in fact for some considerable development will be needed. However, potentially these novel components offer greater functional capabilities.

Decoders

The primary motivation for pursuing the bubble decoders (see Chang et al. [9, pp. 89-93] [98-102]) is to reduce access time and implement on-chip address-

TABLE 17
Views of Subsystem Designers

Long shift register (see above in the sections entitled Current
               Products and Versatility of Shift Registers
               and Major/Minor Loops)
  Open loop
  Recirculating loop
  Dynamic re-allocation
  Cross-switched loops (bubble ladder)
Major/minor loops (see above in the sections entitled Current
               Products and Versatility of Shift Registers
               and Major/Minor Loops)
  Varieties of read/write arrangements
  Cryptographic memory
  Fast-access memory
  Fast-search memory
  Memory to facilitate off-chip associative search
Decoders
  Varieties of read/write/clear arrangements
  Minimum-conductor
  Minimum-power
  Rewriteable decoder
Coincident selection
Associative search
Data management configurations
  Text editing
  Storage management
  Sorting
  Relational data base

---

ability. The major drawback hindering the pursuit of bubble decoders is that in
current designs there is continuous power dissipation throughout the entire duration
of selection and read.

The above remarks can be clarified by comparing the decoders with the major/
minor loops. The access time for the major/minor loops is determined by the
length of the minor loop (usually several hundred field-rotation periods), and the
read time is determined by the length of the major loop (again several hundred
field-rotation periods). A comparable size decoder chip would offer a much shorter
access time (a few tens of periods), but comparable read time, since its access
time is determined by $\log_2$ (number of words) and its read time is proportional to
the data loop length.

Decoders provide on-chip addressability. Thus various functions (memory or
logic) can be spatially distributed in a regular or irregular array, but nevertheless
readily selectable. In contrast, major/minor loops select a group of bits at a time,
select by positioning the bits, and also perform a parallel-to-serial conversion,
thus necessitating a regular array and not adaptable to handling many different
functions.

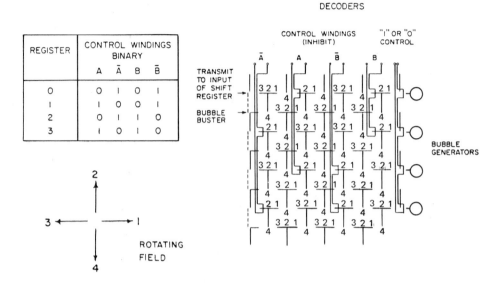

REGISTER	CONTROL WINDINGS BINARY			
	A	Ā	B	B̄
0	0	1	0	1
1	1	0	0	1
2	0	1	1	0
3	1	0	1	0

FIG. 36. Schematic of a write decoder.

The major/minor loops accomplish data transfer in a fraction of one field-rotation period. In between transfers, the switches consume no power. The duty cycle for the switches typically is less than 1%. By contrast, in a decoder the switching currents guide the data throughout the read period (hence high duty cycle

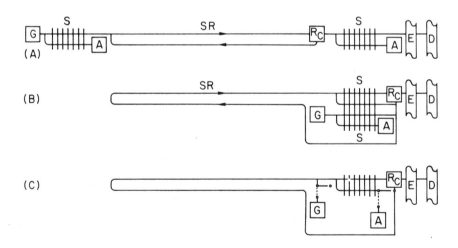

FIG. 37. Evolution of decoder configurations. (a) Separate write (left) and read (right) decoders. No selective clear capability. (b) Combined write and read decoder, with one set of conductors but two sets of switches, to provide selective write, read, and clear capabilities. (c) Combined write and read decoder, with only one set of lines and switches, but sacrificing capability for simultaneous read and write.

for the switches). Worse yet, all words are being scanned simultaneously. Thus all the selection switches are dissipating power at all times.

Obviously, a better decoder design should utilize rewriteable bubble latch switches. Once written, the switches function by bubble-to-bubble interaction and dissipate no power. The rewritability offers the additional advantage of universal parts and easy reconfigurability.

Having reviewed the key issues, we shall now describe some decoder configurations.

A simple write decoder is shown in Fig. 36. Between the 2^n storage shift registers and their respective 2^n generators are n stages of switches which are controlled by n conductor pairs (e.g., 3 conductor pairs to control $2^3 = 8$ shift registers in the figure). The number of stages increases slowly with the increase of the number of shift registers (e.g., 10 conductor pairs to control $2^{10} = 1024$ shift registers). Each stage consists of two complementary columns of switches. Its function is to screen the remaining bubble streams from the previous stage, and let half of them pass while diverting the other half to annihilators. Thus after n stages of switches, only one out of the 2^n identical data streams from the generators will survive and arrive at the selected shift register. Within the decoder, two paths are provided for each generator, one leading toward a storage shift register and the other to an annihilator.

A write decoder can be similarly constructed with all outputs feeding into a chevron-column expander such that the amplification and detection delay is identical for all shift registers.

Several improvements over the simple decoder have been made conceptually. In Fig. 37(a) is shown a section of a complete memory array which consists of the storage shift registers, a write decoder, and a read decoder. Only the parts related to one shift register are shown. The vertical control lines are shared by all shift registers. In Fig. 37(b), the decoding switches are incorporated into the storage array and the write and read functions are made to share the same control lines. In Fig. 37(c), the write and read functions are made to share both the decoding switches and the control lines.

There are four phases during each field rotation in a field-access bubble device. This provides an opportunity to interleave four arrays at quadrature to quadruple the data rate [140]. In Fig. 38 are shown the control conductor configurations which enable each conductor to serve four quadrature arrays on the same chip, thus reducing the number of pads required by the chip. The task is accomplished by placing switches in the four quadrature chips at spatial points corresponding to the same time phase.

The principles of a rewriteable decoder [101] are to be described (Fig. 39). In conventional decoders, a switch is formed by shaping a loop in a conducting line (to concentrate field gradient locally) which traverse all shift registers. By contrast, in a rewriteable decoder, a bubble is placed and held at a locality to provide a switch. In common to both types of decoders, to effect selection a given combination of currents in the conductors for a decoder (i.e., a collection of suitably placed switches) will select a unique shift register. For a conventional decoder, the field gradient of a conductor current alone executes the path switching for data-stream bubbles. In a rewriteable decoder, the combined field gradients of a conductor current and a steering bubble execute the switching. Since the steering bubbles can be loaded and unloaded, the decoder is personalizable and rewriteable.

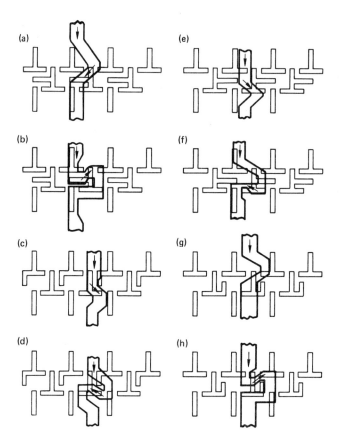

FIG. 38. Switch designs to provide switching in four different shift registers at spatial quadrature but with the same switching current. Each of the four pairs provides a switch (top) and its complement (bottom) for a given quadrature.

The rewriteable decoder is useful as a universal part and a means to avoid defective shift registers.

From the point of view of reducing power dissipation in the switches, loadable switches can be used to reduce the duty cycle [102]. The decoder is implemented by loadable-disk switches instead of current-loop switches. These switches are overlaid with conductors for loading and unloading bubbles. The selection of shift register is again effected by specifying a combination of currents. However, these currents are not used directly to steer data-stream bubbles. Instead, they are used to load bubbles onto disks, which retain bubbles to steer data-stream bubbles. Each time a shift register is selected, the loadable disks must be cleared first by returning the loaded bubbles to holding devices, and then loaded anew with bubbles corresponding to the decoding current specifications. Thus there is no power dissipation during the long period of data transmission, but only during the loading and unloading periods (a fraction of one field-rotation period each).

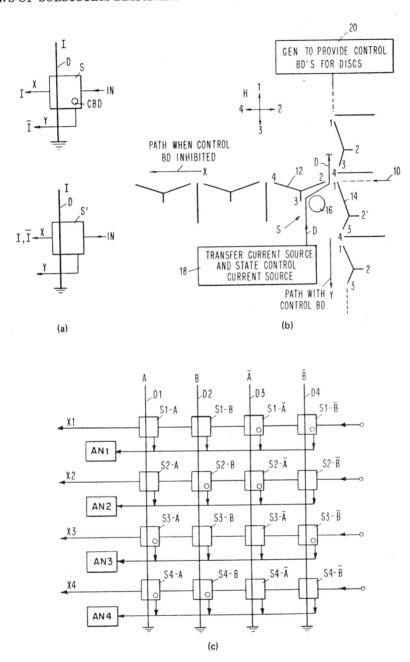

FIG. 39. A rewriteable decoder implemented with Permalloy disks loadable with bubbles. (a) Switch action. (b) Device sketch. (c) Decoder sketch.

Coincident Selection

Bubble chips have high device density and large bit capacity. The entry products already use chips with 100 kbits in a $0.2'' \times 0.2''$ chip area which will evolve into 256 kbit to 1 Mbit chips within a few years. Thus the problem of a small number of pins to serve a large number of bits as encountered by LSI chips will be accentuated in bubble devices.

There is more than one solution to the above problem. One solution is to execute more functions on the chip to avoid unnecessary data output and input. The means are discussed below in the sections entitled Associative Search and Data Management by Bubble Steering. The emphasis is on on-chip data processing and management. The present section describes a solution to extend the major/minor loop organization, emphasizing storage function in large-capacity chips.

A straightforward expansion of a major/minor loop array to incorporate more bits will maintain the same number of interconnection pads. However, the problem is that for an n^2 increase in bit capacity, each shift register will be n times longer attended by an increase in propagation delay from T to nT and a decrease of yield from Y to Y^n. In fact, compounding the yields from both the major and minor loops, the chip yield could degenerate to Y^{2n}.

Our solution is to maintain the same capacity for an individual major/minor loop array but use multiple arrays connected by a coincident selection network (see Bobeck and Scovil [103] and Ahn et al. [104] to enable sharing of pads on the chip and circuits off the chip. The scheme is made possible by the fact that in a major/minor loop array, the selection for read, write, or clear is effected by the activation of both the transfer line and a functional component (detector, generator, or annihilator). Thus, for a matrix of arrays (see Fig. 40), for instance, arrays in the same row may have their transfer lines connected in series, and the arrays in the same column may have their functional lines connected in series. The consecutive activation of a row and a column uniquely selects one array.

Since the signals on these lines are electrical and propagate instantaneously, it is obvious the delays in a chip with conductor-interconnected arrays remain the same as a single array. The interconnecting network could and should be designed with very wide conductors to ensure excellent yield. Thus a large chip with many interconnected arrays will maintain the same yield as a small constituent array. The yield improvement is not only limited to the chip level, it is promulgated into the package level. The net gain in cost/function (i.e., cost/storage bit) is illustrated in Fig. 27(b). (Contrast with Fig. 27a.)

There are prices to be paid and limitations to be observed in the coincident-selection scheme. For an increase in chip capacity by n^2, there will be n arrays by n arrays in the matrix. The number of pads will increase by n (not 2n). A more severe limitation is that n arrays must share a common detector line. While the signal remains the same, both the noise and signal attenuation will increase by n. This limitation imposes an upper limit to the number of arrays accommodable by the coincident selection scheme.

Associative Search

Associative search expands the capability of a memory array much beyond that equipped only with location addressability. See Lee and Chang [105, 106]. While an address represents a single search criterion, the many attributes of a data item provide many possible search criteria. Moreover, they can be used singly or in

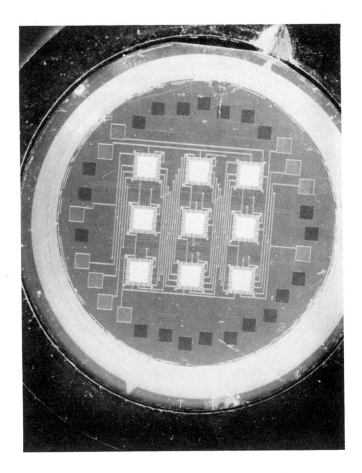

FIG. 40. An example of interconnecting bubble memory arrays for coincident selection (from Ref. 104).

Boolean combinations. While both address selection and content selection are based on exact match, context selection is based on a specified range of values. While address search amounts to identifying a fixed location, associative search reaches many locations simultaneously to look for a match. The use of such capabilities in bubble applications has been described in the context of array logic [106] and data base (see below in the section entitled Data Base). Earlier explorations of associative-search bubble device configurations include Bobeck et al. [107], Murakami [108, 109], and Kluge [110].

Bubble technology is particularly attractive for implementing associative search devices for the following reasons. (1) Although relatively new, it is at the forefront of LSI technologies in terms of large chip capacity, high density, and low power dissipation. Thus it will economically provide 10^8 bit module capacity in the near future, and will potentially grow several orders of magnitude larger. The effectiveness of associative search increases with larger storage capacity. (2) Bubble storages are shift registers. The serial data flow enables the logic needed for associative search to be shared by many bits in a long shift register. The parallel arrangement of shift registers and the perfect synchronization of all devices facilitate the simultaneous actuation of all associative search logic devices. Thus, on a per-bit basis, almost no extra area is needed to accommodate the additional associative search devices. (3) The simple yet versatile hardware implementation should prove more economical than the software implementation of associative search capability.

In terms of implementation, bubble devices have several useful properties: serial access, switching capability, memory capability in switches, etc. To share the search facilities, the memory is organized such that all the words in the memory are searched simultaneously, bit by bit. The search is performed by the interaction of each bubble stream (from each word) and the tag currents (operating on all words), with the results registered in a loadable switch (a latch) provided for each word. After the search, the matched words will keep their passages open for subsequent interrogation, while the mismatched words will have their passages sealed by loading a bubble into a latch, thus preventing interrogation.

The basic element in our bubble associative memory is a Permalloy-disk loadable switch. In general, a bubble switch provides two bubble paths, and the selection of a path can be effected either by a reversal or enhancement of the rotating field, or by current activation, or by residence bubble control (see Chang [9, pp. 44-50]). The residence bubble switch is a switch with memory capability, i.e., a latch. In the following, we shall describe how to use bubble latches to seal off unwanted bubble streams.

A bubble memory consists of shift registers, each of which stores a word. Assume that a bubble represents ONE while a void is ZERO. In the passage between each shift register and the read station, a loadable bubble latch which is controlled by a common transfer/clear line can be inserted. A loadable latch is designed such that when unloaded it will not affect the propagation of bubbles through the passage (see Fig. 41a). It can be loaded with a bubble which is contained in the incoming bubble stream by activating the transfer current (Fig. 41b). Once a latch is loaded, the bubble residing in it will repel incoming bubbles and prevent them from passing through the passage (Fig. 41c). To clear the latches, a clearing current can be applied which simultaneously forces all residing bubbles out of the latches (Fig. 41d).

One embodiment of the passage-sealing mechanism is to use the Permalloy and conductor overlay patterns shown in Fig. 42. A Permalloy disk is used as a bubble latch which will trap a bubble once loaded. The bent T-bar provides a horizontal path without bubble sealing, or a vertical path with bubble sealing. The transfer current is activated during rotation-field phase 2 to prevent a bubble from propagating to the bar while aiding it to travel to the disk (Fig. 42b). When a bubble is loaded onto the disk, it will reside there and force the oncoming bubbles to go down the bent T-bar to an annihilator (Fig. 42c). To clear all the passages, the clear current is activated at phase 4 to drive out the residing bubbles from their disks to annihilators.

Note three features of the loadable-disk latches. First, the passage can be sealed only when a bubble is approaching the latch. Second, the transfer is effected only with the coincidence of the bubble and the activation current. Third, a sealed latch remains sealed until clearing. In the light of these features, an associative-search procedure will be outlined. A sequence of pulses in the transfer current can

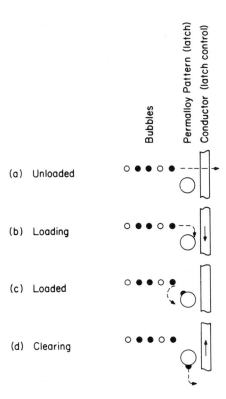

FIG. 41. A latch switch based on bubble-bubble interaction. (a) Bubbles proceed through the latch when it is unloaded. (b) A bubble approaching the latch is being transferred onto the latch by activating the transfer current. (c) Bubbles are detoured by the entrapped bubble on the latch. (d) The entrapped bubble is driven out of the latch by activating the clear current.

be used to represent the tag information. When a tag is specified, all words (i.e., shift registers) which do not have identical tags are to be sealed. The searching consists of the following steps:

1. Use the transfer-current pulses to represent the complemented tag.
2. Interact the bubbles from shift registers with the complement-tag currents at the latches. This will seal off shift registers which contain ONE's where the tag bit is ZERO.
3. Use the transfer-current pulses to represent the tag.
4. Invert the bubble streams from all shift registers before they travel into the latches.
5. Interact the inverted bubble streams with the tag currents at the latches. This will further seal off shift registers which contain ZERO's where the tag bit is ONE.
6. The unsealed shift registers have the specified tags.

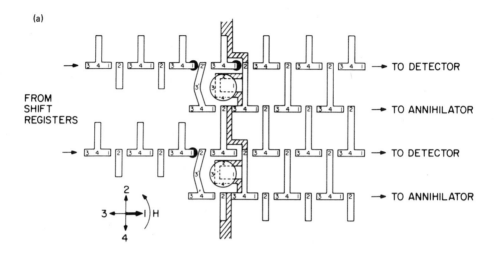

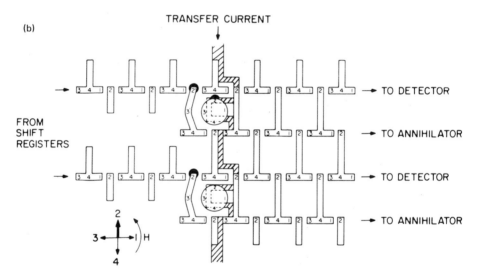

FIG. 42. One embodiment of the latch. (a) Initially, there are no bubbles residing on the disks. (b) A bubble is transferred onto the upper disk by activating the transfer current at phase 2.

(c)

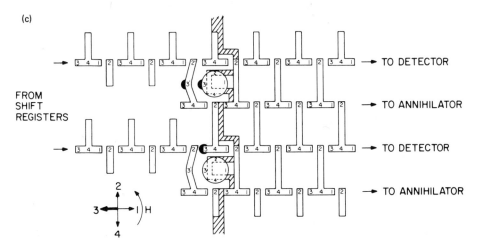

FIG. 42 (continued). (c) During phases 2 and 3 the entrapped bubble will repel the oncoming bubbles to go down the bent T-bar for annihilation, thus sealing the passage.

An example of the associative-search operation is shown in Fig. 43. Observe the three features of the loadable-disk latches enumerated before. During the first cycle, shift registers with ONE's where the tag bits are ZERO's are sealed off. During the second cycle, shift registers with ZERO's where the tag bits are ONE's are sealed off.

Data Management by Bubble Steering

Information in the form of bubbles is in constant motion. It takes little extra effort to direct its flow. Several applications require the rearrangement of data. They include text editing, data topping in a serial storage, sorting, and data base. By selectively incorporating special-type switches, shift registers can be made to perform the above functions.

Text Editing

In current keyboard editing facilities, mechanically accessed magnetic media are used as storage, and electronic logic provides the processing. Data are selected and retrieved from the storage, and placed in a semiconductor memory before manipulation by semiconductor logic. Such an approach requires different technologies and proper interfacing.

Bubbles are becoming a major candidate for low-cost nonvolatile portable storage. We shall demonstrate that minor modifications of the storage shift registers will make them self-sufficient with editing capabilities. It certainly will be attractive to have a storage-editing bubble module (say 10^6 bits for 50 pages of information), even pluggable and exchangeable in a portable typewriter.

The editing of text includes the rearrangement and modification of contents in stored text. The latter consists of clearing and writing, which involves operations

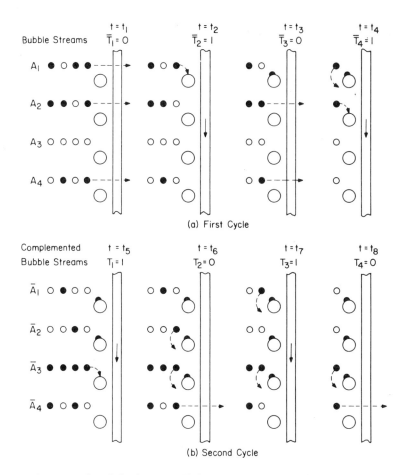

FIG. 43. An example of the bit-parallel associative-search operations. (a) During
the first cycle, a latch is sealed off whenever a ONE (a bubble) in the shift register
coincides with a ZERO (a current) in the tag line. (b) During the second cycle, a
latch is sealed off whenever a ZERO (a bubble) in the shift register coincides with
a ONE (a current) in the tag line. The tags for the four words shown are $A_1 = 1011$,
$A_2 = 1101$, $A_3 = 0000$, and $A_4 = 0101$, respectively. The desired tag is $T = 0101$.

at the I/O port of the shift register. The former consists of deletion, insertion, and
exchange of characters or records.

   The deletion, insertion, or exchange of data always involves the displacement
of a data section (a bit or a record) from the rest. To delete a bit is to clear it and
close the gap it leaves. To insert a bit is to create a bit space and put in a new bit.
To exchange two bits is to freeze the leading bit for a one-bit period and let the
trailing bit bypass.

   A modified shift register suitable for the above operation is shown in Fig. 44.
At its right end, two alternative paths are provided—global and bypass. The right-
end position also serves as the I/O port. Note that the Permalloy pattern at the

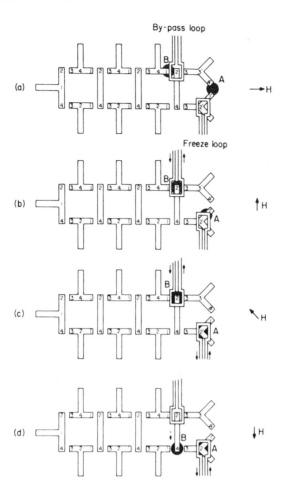

FIG. 44. Successive steps showing the freeze and bypass actions in the editing of a bit string.

right end is designed such that only one bit is stored there. The pattern does not show the I/O facility.

The successive steps in exchanging two adjacent bits are shown in Fig. 44. Initially, bit B follows bit A. During phase 2, the bypass loop is activated to hold B at position 2, while A proceeds. At the start of phase 2', the freeze loop is activated to hold A at position 2'. At phase 4, the bypass current is discontinued to allow B to slide down the I bar to position 4, then the freeze current is discontinued to free A to follow B.

For the insertion operation, the record travels along the bypass path until the new bit is ready to be inserted into the record, and then the global path is followed. For the deletion operation, the record travels along the global path until the designated bit is deleted and then the bypass is followed. Thus only one bit can be inserted or deleted per one-bit period.

The rightmost bit is amenable to freeze action, while
its adjacent bit is amenable to bypass action.

Examples	SR Actions	SR Status
0. Initial status (see Fig. 1a)	1. Idle	EDCBA_H_
1. Exchange B & C	1. Shift 4 bits	A_H_EDCB
	2. Freeze & bypass 1 bit	CA_H_EDB
2. Extract & insert B between D & E	1. Shift 4 bits	A_H_EDCB
	2. Freeze & bypass 2 bits	DCA_H_EB
3. Close gap between E & H	1. Freeze & bypass 1 bit	HEDCBA__
4. Delete C & close gap	1. Shift 5 bits	BA_H_EDC
	2. Clear	BA_H_ED_
	3. Freeze & bypass 4 bits	H_EDBA__
5. Insert a space between B & C	1. Shift 2 bits	H_EDCBA_
	2. Freeze & bypass 2 bits	BAH_EDC_
6. Insert F between B & C	1. Shift 2 bits	H_EDCBA_
	2. Freeze & bypass 2 bits	BAH_EDC_
	3. Write	BAH_EDCF

FIG. 45. Examples of text-editing functions on individual bits.

In principle, any alteration of a record can be effected by a sequence of the above elemental steps of insertion, deletion, and exchange. See Fig. 45. However, for the convenience of editing records, a convertible data structure should be used. Refer to Fig. 46. The structure consists of parallel open-ended shift registers with successive rows propagating in opposite directions. Two columns of switches are provided at the two sides of the parallel shift registers, and an I/O port is provided for the middle pair of shift registers. Now we can describe the insertion and deletion of records which are even multiples of the shift register length.

To insert a record, the existing data is allowed to advance until the record entry point has arrived at the I/O position. Then the upper half of the shift registers are connected into idling mode while the lower half continues to advance. Simultaneously, the new record is entered into the vacated space. When the data insertion is completed, the upper half will be switched into the advance mode. Similarly, to delete a record, the record is allowed to proceed to the I/O position. Then the lower half of the shift registers is connected into the idling mode while the upper half continues to advance to the deletion position. When the data deletion is completed, the lower half will be switched into the advance mode.

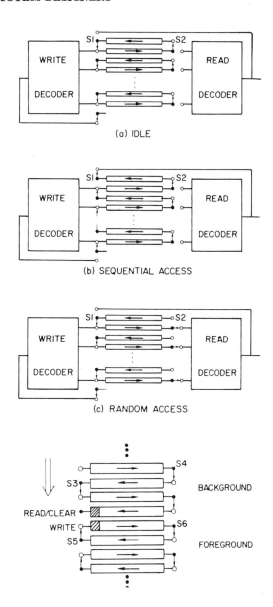

FIG. 46. A convertible structure for editing records. (a) With S1's down and S2's up, the shift registers idle in isolation. (b) With both S1's and S2's up, all shift registers are connected in series for sequential access. (c) With S1's down and S2's to the right, the shift registers are connected to the write decoder to the left and to the read decoder to the right. (d) Read, clear, and write circuits may also be inserted in the middle. With foreground shift registers idling and background shift registers in series and advancing, a record may be deleted without leaving a gap.

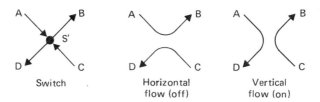

FIG. 47. A flow-steering switch placed at the intersection of four shift registers can effect horizontal flow (A to B, C to D) or vertical flow (A to D, C to B).

Not to be described here but perhaps obvious from the foregoing is that switches can be used to construct editing shift registers for any length of record. A text editing memory system has also been conceptually described in the literature (see Lee and Chang [111]).

Storage Management

In the above section entitled Dynamic Reallocation it has been demonstrated that dynamically reordering shift registers can be used to keep the order of records in storage (hence the order of ease of access) according to their recency of use. Since such a shift register rearranges data on a bit per bit basis, a word of n bits needs

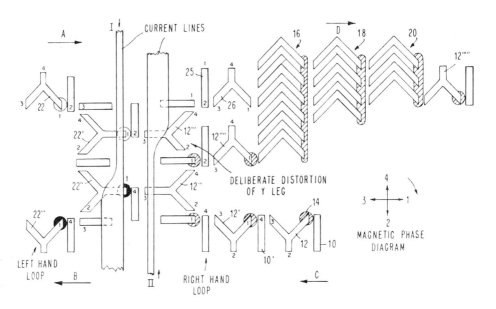

FIG. 48. An implementation of the flow-steering switch by Permalloy-pattern field-access bubble devices. The two conductors execute switching action only where the lines are narrowed over the Permalloy pattern for field concentration. The Permalloy patterns are laid out such that conversion from vertical to horizontal flow (or vice versa) will not lose bits or overlap bits.

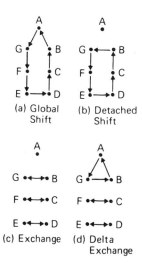

(a) Global   (b) Detached
    Shift   Shift

(c) Exchange   (d) Delta
                    Exchange

FIG. 49. Four basic operations of the bubble ladder.

n such shift registers in parallel with n I/O ports. In the following, structures with
a single I/O port, but capable of efficient record topping, will be described.

   A shift register with switches to facilitate the reordering of records of many
bits (instead of single bits) has been evolved by Tung et al. [112]. The shift register
consists of many loops joined by cross-linking switches. Schematically, a cross-
linking switch is shown in Fig. 47. It has two inputs A and B, and two outputs C
and D. It operates in two modes. In the OFF mode, A and B are linked respectively
to C and D. In the ON mode, A and B are linked respectively to D and C. Two
possible implementations of the cross-linking switch have been proposed. One employs two conductors superimposed on two crossing paths based on an idler. Activation of the conductors switches the outputs between the two output paths. The
other employs a pair of ordinary switches (Fig. 48). In both cases the important
design criterion is that in switching from the OFF to ON mode and vice versa, there
will be no gap and no overlap created in the data flow.

   In the paper by Tung et al. [112], a nonuniform ladder is described. It consists
of many double-record loops topped by a single-record loop. The successive records
are linked by the cross-linking switches into the so-called ladder structure. There
are four modes of operations: global shift (all records shifting along the entire
ladder), bypass shift (all but the top-loop records shifting along the ladder, and the
top loop circulating within itself), exchange (each loop circulating within itself, by
one record), and delta exchange (top loop linked with the adjacent full loop, each of
the other loops closing upon itself). See Fig. 49.

   Although geometrically nonuniform, all the switches (with the possible exception
of the first one) act in unison.

   Chen and Tung [113] also considered a uniform ladder structure which has all
loops equal in length but each holding one record. Although geometrically uniform,
the cross-linking switches are not set uniformly for the cases of interest to us.

   The two different structures have been compared in performing a storage
management function; viz., to top a record a distance d (i.e., d loops) from the top

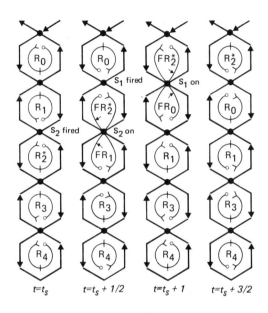

$$t=t_s \qquad t=t_s + 1/2 \qquad t=t_s + 1 \qquad t=t_s + 3/2$$

FIG. 50. Topping operation with slithering in a uniform ladder (after Chen and Tung [113]. The record R^* is to be topped without altering the order of the other records. Each time the head of R^* is approaching a switch, the switch is activated to allow R^* to climb up the next loop.

while preserving the order of all other records. Note the similarity with the dynamic reordering of bits. It can be shown that the record periods required are:

1. Nonuniform ladder   2d
2. Uniform ladder, with exchange   d
3. Uniform ladder, with slithering $(d + 1)/2$
   (see Fig. 50)

In the nonuniform ladder, a suitable combination of the four basic operations under various situations will achieve the topping with reordering operation. In the uniform ladder, the record to be retrieved is always exchanged with the adjacent upper loop until it tops. A more efficient way is to allow the desired record to slither through all the intervening records. A detailed description and analysis are given by Chen and Tung [113].

Sorting
Sorting is a function frequently performed in information processing. As in the case of text editing, it is desirable to perform the sorting function in the storage

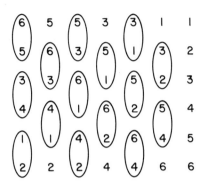

FIG. 51. An illustration of the odd-even sorting scheme. Adjacent records can be paired in two fashions (see odd and even columns). When the odd and even pairing alternate, and each pair is compared to push the smaller member up, the records will be ordered at the end of N cycles (N being the number of items to be sorted).

medium so as to avoid unnecessary data accesses, many I/O ports, many interconnections, and interfacing between different technologies.

The bubble ladder provides a convenient sorting mechanism. Basically, the records are placed in the loops while their corresponding keys are placed in fast semiconductor devices. The keys are compared first and then signals are sent to set the switches to rearrange the bubble records. See Chen et al. [114].

Let us consider a sorting scheme (see Fig. 51): odd-even-transposition sort (OETS). Note that in a linear chain of records (e.g., ABCDE), there are two ways of pairing up the adjacent records (A, BC, DE; or AB, CD, E) covering all but the two end items. The odd-even-transposition scheme uses the two pairing schemes in alternation. Within each pairing scheme the two operands in each pair are compared and rearranged if necessary to achieve a prescribed local ordering.

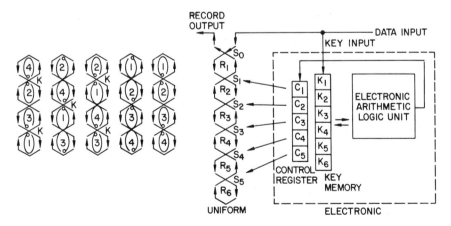

FIG. 52. Sorting by bubble ladder. The keys are sorted by semiconductor devices. The bulk of the storage is then rearranged by the bubble ladder structure based on the information generated by key sorting.

It has been proven that for N records to be sorted completely, N pairing-permutation stages will suffice. By contrast, other schemes would require an (N log N) time period. However, the timing economy is gained at the expense of large numbers of hardware. For N records to be sorted in a pipelined fashion, $N(N - 1)/2$ comparators, N^2 record space, and N I/O ports are required.

A bubble ladder circulates the records and makes them pass through the cross-linking switches repeatedly, thus permitting the repeated use of (N - 1) comparators (rather than $N(N - 1)/2$), a linear space (rather than 2D space), and a single I/O port. The implementation and its operation are shown in Fig. 52.

Data Base

As has already been demonstrated amply in previous sections, bubbles possess considerable data manipulation capability. One could make some general and qualitative assessment to match the capability of bubbles with the requirements of data base. Let us explore four properties of bubble memories—modularity, associativity, electronic timing, and structured storage.

From memory modules, to chips, to grouping of shift registers on a chip, to the many words contained in a group of shift registers, a bubble memory provides many levels of modularity of data, both in terms of storage and in terms of selective access. The electronic seeking time (or access time) for bubbles is shorter than the mechanical seeking time for disk files. More importantly, the scan time for a modular data unit (at the right level) is much shorter than the scan time for half-a-million serial bits per track as usually encountered in a disk file. Furthermore, modular data units permit parallel accessing and parallel processing.

An associative bubble memory device was discussed above in the section entitled Associative Search. On-chip associative cells enable simultaneous search of all data, and the output of only qualified data. Even when the associative search has to be performed off-chip, the selection of an appropriate data block still reduces the access and search time.

Electronic timing will further enhance the associative search in a significant manner. Let us consider the use of marker loops incorporated in the control unit for the bubble memory. These loops could be of the same length and synchronized with the minor loops. In disk files, marker bits are interspersed with and in series with the data bits. This practice ensures synchronization, but carries with it the penalty of having to traverse all the data (hence incurring unnecessary delays) when the marker bits are to be examined. The marker bits in bubble memories, being in parallel and in synchronization with the data shift registers, permit repeated scanning and marking in performing complicated repetitive search processes. Being separate from the data bits, the marker bits can be quickly scanned in order to decide what records are qualified to be read. The proper use of marker loops provides a way to construct indices and pointers dynamically on any of a collection of attributes. Its use does not carry the penalty of making updating a difficult process.

Bubble memories are structured arrays with the locations defining data units and conditioning access methods. This is in contrast to disk files which require data formatting to define each of the long continuous tracks, the units of data, their characteristics, etc. Let us illustrate how the regular bubble memory structure can be of use in implementing a relational data base. The relational data model views data in the form of a table, with a set of similar entries arranged in rows and their many attributes aligned in columns. A data base consists of many such

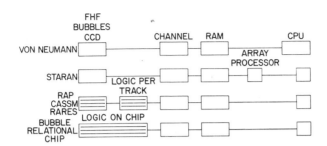

FIG. 53. Evolution toward intelligent storage for data base applications. (a) In
the beginning, data base processing was conducted in the CPU of the conventional
computer architectured for computation. (b) In STARAN, the data base processing
is separated from the CPU and implemented in an array processor. (c) Inexpensive
semiconductor components have made possible logic-per-track architectures (e.g.,
RAP, CASSM, RARES), which shift much of the data base processing close to the
storage device (fixed-head disks and, in the future, bubbles or CCD's). (d) Ulti-
mately, parallel-associative-search devices could be implemented on bubble storage
chips to provide many of the data base operations in the intelligent storage.

tables. The items in the table may vary with time because of modifications, inser-
tions, and deletions. Data in two or more tables can be interrelated through compatible attributes which appear in each of the tables. Queries to the data can be
considered as selecting data and structuring a new table. It is obvious that an array-
like memory has a natural affinity to a table-like data base.

    With the advances in LSI devices for processing and storage, the architecture
for data base is evolving from centralized processing on the CPU to the executing
of data base functions close to or in storage (see Fig. 53). Bubbles will particularly
facilitate distributed storage and processing. Two magnetic-bubble memory chips
have been proposed for relational-model associative-search data base applications.
The first one (see Chang [115]) employs bubble-ladder shift registers in parallel
for storage (Fig. 54). Each is connected to an associative search cell, and all associative cells are subject to the control of the same set of search conductors. The
cross-linked loops provide distinct and interchangeable columns. When a decoder
is used, all rows are equally accessible and thus could be considered interchangeable. The on-chip search capability enables both quick simultaneous search and the
reduction of chip output to qualified data only. It has been demonstrated that such
chips can execute Cartesian product, union, intersection, difference, projection,
join, and restriction, thus providing complete selection capability for interrogate
and update.

    The second approach (see Chang and Nigam [116]) avoids the use of novel com-
ponents such as bubble-ladder and associative-search devices. It is mainly based
on the conventional major/minor loop arrays, but with a significant modification
(Fig. 55). The transfer conductor in the major loop is divided into several sections
which can be driven separately or in combination. Thus the minor loops are divided into
groups for separate accesses. Each group can be accessed and scanned much faster
than the entire chip. Off-chip associative-search devices and marker loops are
provided. For complex queries which require successive searches on different
domains (different groups of minor loops), the intermediate results of a search can

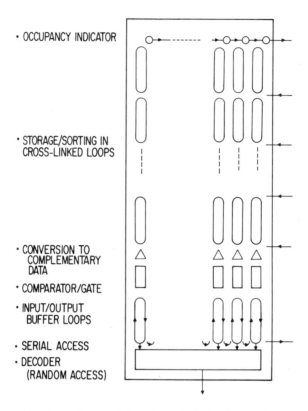

- OCCUPANCY INDICATOR

- STORAGE/SORTING IN
  CROSS-LINKED LOOPS

- CONVERSION TO
  COMPLEMENTARY
  DATA

- COMPARATOR/GATE

- INPUT/OUTPUT
  BUFFER LOOPS

- SERIAL ACCESS

- DECODER
  (RANDOM ACCESS)

FIG. 54. Schematic of a relational data base bubble chip with on-chip parallel-associative-search capability, which should provide performance superior to current implementations. An example of such devices is described in Figs. 42 and 43.

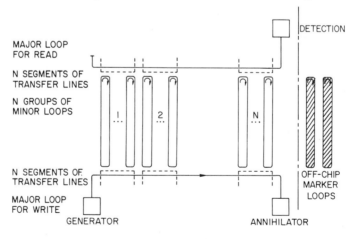

MAJOR LOOP
FOR READ

N SEGMENTS OF
TRANSFER LINES

N GROUPS OF
MINOR LOOPS

N SEGMENTS OF
TRANSFER LINES

MAJOR LOOP
FOR WRITE

GENERATOR   ANNIHILATOR

DETECTION

OFF-CHIP
MARKER
LOOPS

FIG. 55. For near-term implementation, both hardware structure (major/minor loops) and data structure (tabular) could be utilized to provide a relational-model data base. This approach facilitates access for serial associative search and economizes input/output operations.

be registered in the marker loops. The scan of marker loops directs the skipping of tuples already disqualified based on previous searches. Cross-marking can also be used for queries involving multiple relations (or multiple chips). Again, both the search time and output time are greatly reduced.

Recent literature on data base is quite extensive; interested readers may start with the review article by Hsiao and Madnick [117]. However, it appears that much remains to be done to explore the intrinsic attributes of the new technologies for novel architecture.

Views of System Architects

The promise of bubble mass storage devices at cost comparable to disks but offering much shorter access time has elicited qualitative discussions, although not quantitative assessment of improved or novel system architectures. Table 18 is a summary of Wensley's paper [118].

When disks are used as backing stores for main memories, the great discrepancy between their access speeds has forced the adoption of many subterfuges in terms of paging systems, complex algorithms, very fast channels, and multiple units to achieve a reasonable throughput in the computer. The replacement of disks by bubbles could have the following impacts on system architecture.

Time-Sharing Systems with Central Shared Large Memory and Multiple Miniprocessors

A large-capacity bubble memory can obtain fast access speed by dynamically reordered shift registers (see above in the section entitled Dynamic Reallocation) or better still by bubble ladders (see above in the section entitled Data Management by Bubble Steering). It could be used for the central memory to store system programs such as compilers, assemblers, and loaders, and also to store user data.

TABLE 18
Views of System Architects

Time-sharing systems (multiple miniprocessors + large central memory)
   Central memory for large system programs (compilers, assemblers, loaders, etc.)
   Simple operating system, fault isolation, security and privacy
Stand-alone minicomputers and microcomputers (with large memory)
   Slow processor but large memory (business applications need not be fast but need access to a large number of programs)
Main-memory as cache, bubbles for main data storage
   Main-memory speed at bubble-storage capacity and cost advantage
Batch processing with buffering of all I/O operations
   Buffering to maintain even flow of workload
   No multiprogramming, simple operating system and scheduling
Transaction-oriented data processing
   Large storage to support processing each transaction as it comes
   Reduction of processing time

The scheduling of jobs on such a system is simplified to space sharing in the central memory and the resolution of conflicts between processors. The end results would be simpler operating system, fault isolation, and data security and privacy.

Stand-Alone Minicomputers with Large Memory

Business data processors do not need speed but need access to a large number of programs. Thus large capacity but slow memory will be adequate. This application departs from the traditional coupling of a large memory to a fast processor.

Main-Memory as Cache and Bubble Memory for Data Storage

The system will provide storage capacity of the bubble memory but the speed of the main memory.

Buffers, Paging Devices, and File Storage

As a buffer between the central processing unit and slower peripheral units, a bubble memory which is fast enough to transmit data and large enough to hold many data records will accomplish a more constant job flow.

In multiprogrammed computers, whenever one job cannot continue due to unavailability of program or data, another job is run on the processor and the missing data is fetched by a paging device. However, when a paging device with essentially zero access time becomes available, it would not be necessary to switch jobs. Instead, a transfer would be initiated from the bubble storage while the processor is made to wait for a short time (say 100 μsec). If multiprogramming is still desired (e.g., in a time-sharing system to maintain service to many terminals), the control of that process can be separated from the control of the information flow, resulting in simplification of the operating system.

As the bubble storage becomes cheap enough to hold files (at least small- and medium-size files), it will offer increased access speed. The use of the same technology both for the main file device and the paging device would further simplify the operating system.

Batch-Processing with Buffering of all I/O Operations

In large batch data processing systems, a large bubble memory could be used as a buffer for all I/O data. As a consequence, the central processor need not be multiprogrammed for efficient utilization, thus simplifying the operating system and the job scheduling.

Views of Programmers

Computer hardwares become useful tools in the hands of users only when algorithms and programs have been prepared. In most conventional uses, bubble memories could be treated as electronic disks and tapes. As has been pointed out above in the section entitled Varieties of Read/Write Arrangements, the major/minor loops can emulate a disk file, and a recirculatory shift register or major/minor loops with "mutually prime" minor loop design can emulate a tape loop. In such direct emulations, many of the features of programs developed for disks and tapes could be utilized. However, there are unique features available to bubbles

TABLE 19
Views of Programmers

Dual speed (clock rate under program control)
    Algorithms based on perfect shuffle permutation (e.g., fast transforms,
      sorting, matrix transposition)
Start and stop (on and off under program control)
    Algorithms optimized for tapes also applicable here (e.g., large
      systems of linear differential equations by matrix scan)
Bidirectional (direction under program control)
    At uniform speed
      Algorithms utilizing efficient forward and backward scanning of data
      (e.g., linear and partial differential equations)
    With start/stop
      Algorithms based on push-down stack behavior
      Algorithms requiring backward read capability (e.g., "tape" sorting)

---

but not to disks and tapes. The electronic timing of the bubble memory operation places the system under program control at all times. The capabilities of dual (or multiple) speeds, instantaneous start or stop, and bidirectional access to data give bubble memories unique opportunities to construct new programs and algorithms. As sizable bubble storage subsystems are not yet available to the users, there has been little programming consideration given to bubbles. Stone [119] has made a good start. Table 19 is an extract from his paper.

Dual-Speed Memory

When data rates can be selected to be R or 2R under program control, algorithms more efficient than those for disks can be constructed to execute fast transforms, data sorting, and matrix transpose. Four memories with two serving as inputs at data rate R and two as outputs at data rate 2R and with inputs and outputs alternating can function as a perfect shuffle [120]. It serves as the basis for the fast Fourier transform [121, 122], fast Hadamard transform, and sorting.

The dual-speed cyclic memory also makes it possible to transpose a matrix from a format that supports row-by-row scan into one that supports column-by-column scan, and the transformation costs only O (log N) passes of the data [123]. The two-dimensional matrix is stored linearly. Thus, for a matrix X of the size 2^n by 2^n, an element X[i, j] is displaced from X[0, 0] by $(i2^n + j)$ in row major order, but by $(j2^n + i)$ in column major order. To transpose the matrix is to change the displacement.[1] It can be shown that the transpose can be effected by n perfect shuffles.

Start-Stop Memory

A bubble memory can be made to advance one word position with each read or write, and otherwise be stationary, under program control. Such a memory

---

[1]It should be noted that bubble devices can be organized as a two-dimensional memory to allow both row access and column access, thus eliminating the need for transpose.

simulates the behavior of a magnetic tape and can utilize the algorithms developed for tapes but with speed improvement (better than standard or dual-speed cyclic memories). For example, to sort an array of size N requires (see Knuth [124]):

N passes   by mechanical drum

$(\log_2 N)^2$ passes   by dual-speed memory

$(\log_2 N)$ passes   by start-stop cyclic memory (e.g., 4-tape merge sort)

Note that the odd-even transposition sorting scheme as adapted to bubble ladders by Chen et al. [114] (described briefly above in the section entitled Data Management by Bubble Steering) only requires the delay of 1 pass (i.e., time to traverse over all N records).

It is conjectured that cyclic start-stop memories facilitate the construction of efficient algorithms by organizing data blocks into many independent shift registers, each under separate clock control. Thus each block can be scanned sequentially at a rate determined by the program. With this viewpoint many algorithms written for computers with auxiliary tape memories could be adapted to computers with bubble memories. Pavkovich's algorithm [125] for solving large systems of linear equations is one such example. Some algorithms developed for page-memory environments created by rotating magnetic memories also apply to cyclic start-stop memories (see Coffman and McKeller [126] and Moler [127]).

Bidirectional Memories

The direction of data flow can be reversed by the reversal of field rotation in a bubble memory. For some algorithms a programmed bidirectional scan of data is an essential aspect to attain high computation speed. They include Forsythe and Moler's [128] linear equation solvers for band matrices, Young's [129] SSOR iterative method for solving certain partial differential equations, and an algorithm for solving large Poisson problems on rectangular areas [130].

Bidirectional start-stop memories can simulate push-down stacks. Each write in the forward direction corresponds to a push-down operation, and a read in the reverse direction then recovers the last item pushed. This memory is more powerful than the tape memories since it allows data entry at any internal point, whereas a tape memory can only add new data at the end. It should be noted that the bubble ladder [112] is a more versatile memory which is capable of FIFO and FILO operations without bidirectionality or start-stop (see above in the section entitled Data Management by Bubble Steering). The bubble ladder utilizes the intrinsic switch capability of bubble devices. Some sorting algorithms and an ALGOL compiler for CDC memories utilize stack and background read capabilities [124, pp. 301-320].

PERFORMANCE

There are ascending levels of hardware (from devices to chips to systems) and corresponding measures of performance (essentially speed). It is the purpose of this section to relate the measures of speed to the hardware designs at various levels. See Table 20.

At the device level (viz., shift registers and their accessories, e.g., detectors), the speed is measured in terms of data rate. The determining factors of data

TABLE 20
Hardware Levels, Speed Measures, and Determining Factors

Hardware level	Speed measure	Determining factors
Devices	Data rate	Storage medium Device designs Packaging designs

Chips	Access time	Chip organizations
		  Major/minor loops
		  Decoders
		  Coincident selection
		  Dynamic ordering
		  Bubble ladders

System	Task time	General purpose
		  Storage hierarchy
		    Access time
		    Block transfer time
		    Paging, swapping
		  Queueing
		Special purpose
		  Text editing
		  Sorting
		  Data base

rate are storage medium characteristics (domain wall velocities, temperature insensitivity, long-term operation integrity, etc.), device designs (the interleaving of shift registers, etc.) and packaging designs (minimization of time constant and power dissipation in drive coils, etc.).

At the chip level (i.e., the collection of shift registers sharing I/O pads), the high degree of configurability as made possible by switches et al. has given rise to a rich variety of chip organizations. The major purpose of these organizations is to achieve short access time.

It is interesting to contrast bubble storage with mechanical-access disk storage. Chips are more amenable to parallel operation (thus achieving high system data rate even at a modest device data rate), and start/stop operation (thus positioning data for next access rather than catching flying data in intermittent fashion). With coincident selection, the bit capacity on a chip is increased while maintaining the same access time. The traditional constraint of trading access time for capacity in disk files is greatly reduced in bubble technology. Even more interesting are the dynamic-ordering and bubble-ladder devices. They enable data management on the chip to improve the access time.

At the system level (i.e., the collection of chips plus accessories), the speed is measured in terms of how long it takes to perform a task. It appears appropriate to consider separately general-purpose systems and special-purpose systems. In the former the bubble storage will be fit into the general framework of storage hierarchy, multiprogramming, multiprocessing, etc. The evaluation and simulation methodologies as evolved in the past are by and large useful in assessing the performance of storage systems containing bubbles.

The synopses of the earlier evaluations are given in Chang's book [9, Sections 3.2.3 and 3.3]. In addition, Bhandarkar and Juliussen [45] have discussed the advantages of start/stop and bidirectional shift capabilities, memory controller and software simplicities, and illustrative system performance evaluation by a queueing model. In essence, if the memory system can be divided into a number of independent modules, each can be stopped at its last access location, then memory allocation algorithms can be designed to load the various subprograms of a job in co-adjacent addresses. It is then expected that successive accesses to a submodule will be separated by a smaller distance, thus improving the overall waiting time. Bidirectional shifting is expected to halve the minor-loop average delay time. The simplicity in controller is relative to disk files, which have critical timing relations for data transfer and intricate addressing methods. A bubble controller is estimated to be simpler (hence cheaper) by a factor of 2 to 4. Other bubble features such as the freedom from data formatting and ease of interrupt handling will simplify software in terms of controller microprograms, I/O channel programming, and operating system I/O operations, obviously reducing task execution time in the system. The use of a queueing model on bubble storage systems has also been reported by Bonyhard and Hagedorn [131] using a shortest-seek-time-first request scheduling algorithm to improve request throughput. Pohm et al. [50] have evaluated modified major/minor loop chips in two-level and three-level memory hierarchies. The minor loops are provided with short intermediate loops as buffers to the major loop. Prestaging in the intermediate loops improves effective cycle time. Jino and Liu [132] have analyzed the average word retrieval time and average page retrieval time for memory systems using major/minor loop or decoder chips by varying data arrangement from bit per chip to word per chip to page per chip, as well as by varying word size, chip size, and total capacity. The performance analysis of the bubble ladder as an N-level storage hierarchy has been studied by Chen and Tung [113] and Chen and Chang [133].

The innovative special-purpose applications of bubble storage offer performance beyond the conventional measures. In essence, data processing capability is added to the storage, which is then called intelligent memory in some publications. We cite three examples here: text editing, sorting, and data base. While it still takes time to perform these tasks, it is not measured in terms of data block access time, hit ratio, paging time, and swapping time. These tasks are performed within the storage media, and only the final processed data are retrieved from the chips. Much of the input/output operations to and from the processing unit is eliminated. Pipelined or parallel operations are inherent in the algorithms and hardware operations.

It is also important to point out that while the special-purpose applications require specially designed chips or modifications of general-purpose chips, nevertheless such special or modified chips can be kept amenable to general-purpose storage.

SUMMARY

To conclude, we shall remark on bubble technology in the time frames of the present, the near future, and the distant future.

It has taken longer than expected to bring the technology to the marketplace. The strongholds of established semiconductor and disk technologies are very much in evidence. However, what we see as the first-generation bubble products are respectable entries. The 10^5-bit chips exceed the bit capacity of competitive semiconductor chips, and offer a modularity not economically available in floppy disks. The portable data entry terminals provide sizable nonvolatile storage not available from semiconductors, and the ruggedness and portability not available from floppy disks.

This dual competition with semiconductors and disks will continue into the future. Let us first look at the near future. From the fabrication point of view, there is sufficient evidence that 10^6-bit bubble chips could be produced, and the price per bit is estimated at $0.01¢$, which represents a ten-time decrease in price from the present bubble products.

From the application point of view, the NASA-Rockwell space recorder will be a significant step forward. In comparison with disks, it provides fixed-head-file bit capacity (10^8 bits) but with greatly reduced volume and weight; it improves reliability by eliminating mechanical motion and allows the memory to operate in segments. In comparison with semiconductors, the power dissipation is intrinsically much lower, and the nonvolatile storage requires no back-up battery in case of power failure. In the near future the flexibility and versatility of bubble memory chips will also be explored. Significant performance enhancement will be achieved not by significant changes in functional components, but by incremental modification of the chip organization of long shift registers and major/minor loops.

The distant future of bubbles holds greater fascination for us. We presented a technical argument why the fast pace of progress in integrated-circuit technologies will continue without abating (at least with bubbles) in the coming decade and beyond. Clever bubble device designs will achieve densities a hundred times higher than present devices even if the fabrication facilities are limited to photolithography. The emerging electron beam lithography would allow scale-down of all devices, again by orders of magnitude. The steady progress in wafer fabrication and device processing allows additional improvement. In sum, we could say that should business considerations dictate a factor of 2 improvement in chip capacity per year throughout the next 15 years (as it did in the past 15 years), the technology is not bound by intrinsic limitations but is rather endowed with an expandable technical basis to sustain the expected progress.

The pending appearance of 10^6-bit chips by the end of the decade already calls for innovation in chip organization to maintain or upgrade performance and for innovative uses of bubble storage. The steady and predictable progress toward a 10^9-bit chip in another decade provides a great opportunity to rethink and implement strategies in storage subsystems, in computer architectures, and to continually rebalance software and hardware. Integrated circuit technologies in the past have been said to derive their success from the integration of the various technical disciplines to achieve the integration of the circuits. With a chip growing in capacity not only to embody a collection of circuits, but to engulf a subsystem or even a system, design forethought is required to embrace the full spectrum from device physics and processing to system functions and architecture. In this respect we are far from mature in our thinking, but we have made an attempt to bring together the existing body of knowledge uttered on behalf of bubbles. Many unconventional bubble devices are presented. The views by subsystem designers, architects, and programmers are collected.

The raw speed of bubble devices as measured in data rate is basically determined by storage medium and drive-coil characteristics. The various chip organizations achieve greater parallelism in data storage than single shift registers, thus reducing significantly the access time. Moreover, as additional benefits from the development of more functional chips to better utilize the bit capacity, the organization and operation of such chips could reduce the time required to perform certain system functions (e.g., text editing time, query time).

The future of bubbles indeed appears bright, but significant efforts will be required to realize the full potential. The author hopes that he has introduced the readers to the many enticing opportunities and challenging problems in store for bubbles.

REFERENCES

1. A. Clogstron, Solid-state physics and magnetic bubble technology, originally published in The Core Subfields of Physics, by National Academy of Sciences, Washington, D.C., 1972; more accessible as a reprint in Magnetic Bubble Technology, H. Chang, IEEE Press, 1975, pp. 221-225.
2. C. Kooy and U. Enz, Experimental and theoretical study of the domain configuration in thin layers of $BaFe_{12}O_{19}$, Philips Res. Rep. 15, 7-29 (1960).
3. A. H. Bobeck, Properties and device applications of magnetic domains in orthoferrites, Bell Syst. Tech. J. 46, 1901-1925 (October 1967).
4. Texas Instruments, Magnetic Bubble Memories and System Interface Circuits from Texas Instruments (Tentative Data), February 1977, available from TI Inc., P.O. Box 5012, Mail Station 308, Dallas, Texas 75222.
5. J. E. Geusic, Magnetic bubble devices: Moving from laboratory to factory, Bell Lab. Rec. 54(11), 263-267 (November 1976).
6. A. H. Bobeck, R. F. Fischer, and J. L. Smith, An overview of magnetic bubble domains—material-device interface, in Proceedings of the AIP 17th Annual Conference on Magnetism and Magnetic Materials, American Institute of Physics, New York, 1971, pp. 45-55.
7. P. I. Bonyhard and J. L. Smith, 68 k-bit capacity 16 μm-period magnetic bubble memory chip design with 2 μm minimum features, IEEE Trans. Magn. 12(6), 614-617 (November 1976).
8. A. H. Bobeck, P. I. Bonyhard, and J. E. Geusic, Magnetic bubbles—An emerging new memory technology, Proc. IEEE 63(8), 1176-1195 (August 1975).
9. H. Chang, Magnetic Bubble Technology—Integrated-Circuit Magnetics for Digital Storage and Processing, IEEE Press, Wiley, New York, 1975.
10. I. Tsuboya, M. Saito, T. Hattanda, N. Yamaguchi, and Y. Arai, 2 Mbit magnetic bubble memory, IEEE Trans. Magn. 13(5), 1360-1363 (September 1977).
11. J. E. Juliussen, D. M. Lee, and G. M. Cox, Bubbles appearing as microprocessor storage, Electronics 50(16), 81-86 (August 4, 1977).
12. J. E. Juliussen, Bubble memory as small mass storage, in Proceedings of the IEEE Electro '77, IEEE, New York, 1977, Paper 12.5.
13. J. W. Nielsen, Bubble domain memory materials, IEEE Trans. Magn. 12(4), 327-345 (July 1976).

14. J. L. Archer, Megabit bubble chip, INTERMAG Conf. Dig. June 1977, Paper 11.1.

15. D. C. Bullock, M. S. Shaikh, and F. G. West, Magnetic bubble device processing and pickax circuit design, IEEE Trans. Magn. 12(6), 654-656 (November 1976).

16. R. E. Fontana, D. C. Bullock, J. T. Carlo, S. K. Singh, M. S. Shaikh, and J. L. Bartelt, Design, processing, and operation of full function, double level, field access test circuits for 2 micron diameter bubbles, INTERMAG Conf. Dig. June 1977, Paper 11.2.

17. B. Stein, H. Callen, M. Casey, and R. Josephs, Effect of Elastic Properties of SiO₂ Spacer on Bubble Pinning, presented at the 23rd Annual Conference on Magnetism and Magnetic Materials, November 1977, Abstract 3A.3.

18. D. K. Ros⌐ Planar processing for magnetic bubble devices, IEEE Trans. Magn. 12(b), 618-621 (November 1976).

19. D. J. Hayes, A 92 k single chip bubble memory package, INTERMAG Conf. Dig. June 1977, Paper 21.6.

20. G. P. Vella-Colerio and W. E. Hess, The generation of rotating magnetic fields for bubble devices, IEEE Trans. Magn. MAG-10, 750-752 (September 1974).

21. M. Takasu, H. Maegawa, T. Sukeda, and K. Yamagishi, Reflection coil packaging for bubble devices, IEEE Trans. Magn. MAG-11, 1151-1153 (September 1975).

22. F. J. Becker and R. L. Stermer, Packaging of a large capacity magnetic bubble domain in spacecraft recorder, Spring CompCon '77, Dig. Pap. pp. 258-262.

23. F. F. Judd, L. H. Young, and P. C. Michaelis, Analysis of rotating fields in magnetic bubble drive coils, IEEE Trans. Magn. 12(6), 642-644 (1976).

24. R. J. Radner and J. H. Wuroinen, Jr., Magnetic bubble serial data store, in 1976 IEEE International Solid-State Circuits Conference, Winner, New York, 1976, pp. 178-179.

25. N. Saito, T. Toyooka, S. Yoshizawa, and Y. Sugita, A high speed drive coil for a large capacity bubble memory, IEEE Trans. Magn. 12(6), 639-641 (1976).

26. J. T. Carlo, A. D. Stephenson, and D. J. Hayes, Chip packaging efficiency in bubble modules, IEEE Trans. Magn. 12(6), 624-628 (1976).

27. W. J. DeBonte and R. Zappulla, Relationship of bias field setting procedure to field stability against external field perturbations for magnetic bubble memory bias field structures, IEEE Trans. Magn. 12(5), 645-648 (1976).

28. W. J. DeBonte and A. D. Butherus, Temperature dependence of Ba-ferrite bubble memory bias magnets as a function of magnet geometry, IEEE Trans. Magn. 12(6), 648-650 (1976).

29. W. J. DeBonte and A. D. Butherus, Magnetically permeable adhesives and adhesive-joined magnetic shield structures, IEEE Trans. Magn. 13(5), 1376-1378 (September 1977).

30. E. Y. Yu, Thermal characteristics of a four-chip magnetic bubble package, IEEE Trans. Magn. 13(5), 1373-1375 (September 1977).

31. P. W. Shumate, P. C. Michaelis, and R. J. Peirce, Long term propagation studies in magnetic-bubble devices, in Proceedings of the AIP 19th Annual Conference on Magnetism and Magnetic Materials, American Institute of Physics, New York, 1973, pp. 140-151.

32. F. B. Hagedorn, L. F. Rago, D. E. Kish, Y. S. Chen, W. E. Hess, H. R. Beurrier, and D. P. Wagner, Magnetic bubble device testing, IEEE Trans. Magn. 13(5), 1364-1370 (September 1977).

33. T. Ferrio, R. Keenan, and R. Naden, Magnetic bubble memory testing, Digital Des. pp. 69-77 (June 1977).

34. R. A. Naden, Longevity and error rate measurements of 92 kbit bubble devices, INTERMAG Conf. Dig. June 1977, Paper 21.4.

35. J. E. Williams, Magnetic bubble memory in telephone systems, in Proceedings of the IEEE Electro '77, IEEE, New York, 1977, Paper 12.3.

36. T. M. Burford, Applications of serial bubble memory, INTERMAG Conf. Dig. June 1977, Paper 29.2.

37. E. A. Buvinger and S. E. Cummins, Military applications of magnetic bubble memory, in Proceedings of the IEEE Electro '77, IEEE, New York, 1977, Paper 12.2.

38. T. T. Chen, O. D. Bohning, L. R. Tocci, J. L. Archer, and R. L. Stermer, A magnetic bubble domain flight recorder, IEEE Trans. Magn. 10(3), 739-745 (September 1974).

39. E. J. Hoffman, R. C. Moore, and T. L. McGovern, Designing a magnetic bubble data recorder: Part I—The component level, and Part II—The system level, Comput. Des. 15(3), 77-88 (March 1976); 15(4), 99-109 (April 1976).

40. R. L. Stermer, Bubble memories for spacecraft data recorders, INTERMAG Dig. 1977, Paper 29.1.

41. W. C. Mavity, Bubble memory system applications, in Proceedings of the IEEE Electro '77, IEEE, New York, 1977, Paper 12.4.

42. J. E. Juliussen, Magnetic bubble memory interfacing, in CompCon '75 Fall Digest of Papers, IEEE, New York, September 1975.

43. D. M. Lee, Bubble memory for microprocessor mass storage, in CompCon '77 Spring Digest of Papers, IEEE, New York, September 1975.

44. R. A. Naden and F. G. West, Fault tolerant memory organization: Impact on chip yield and system cost, IEEE Trans. Magn. 10(3), 852-855 (September 1974).

45. D. P. Bhandarkar and J. E. Juliussen, Tutorial: Computer system advantages of magnetic bubble memories, Computer 8(11), 35-40 (1975).

46. Texas Instruments, Bubble Memory Controller TMS9916JL, February 1977, available from TI Inc., P.O. Box 5012, Mail Station 308, Dallas, Texas 75222.

47. J. S. Flannigan, Bubble memory terminal, an added dimension for data entry, in CompCon Fall '77 Digest of Papers, September 6-9, 1977, pp. 90-93.

48. W. F. Beausoleil, D. T. Brown, and B. E. Phelps, Magnetic bubble memory organization, IBM J. Res. Dev. 16, 587 (1972).

49. P. I. Bonyhard and T. J. Nelson, Dynamic data reallocation in bubble memories, Bell Syst. Tech. J. 52, 307 (1973).

50. A. V. Pohm, M. L. Covault, and S. R. Doctor, Bubble memories for microcomputers and minicomputers, IEEE Trans. Magn. 12(6), 636-638 (November 1976).

51. J. E. Ypma, I. S. Gergis, and J. L. Archer, 64k fast access chip design, in AIP Conference Proceedings No. 34, American Institute of Physics, New York, 1976, pp. 51-53.

52. Y. S. Lin, C. N. Liu, and D. T. Tang, Cryptographic magnetic bubble domain memory, U.S. Patent 3,990,060 (filed March 27, 1974; issued November 2, 1976).

53. A. H. Bobeck and R. F. Fischer, Magnetic bubble PROM memory, U.S. Patent 4,021,791 (filed April 20, 1076; issued May 3, 1977).

54. G. E. Moore, Progress in digital integrated electronics, in Proceedings of the International Electronic Devices Meeting, Washington, D.C., December 1975.

55. R. N. Noyce, From relays to MPU's, Computer 9(12), 26-29 (December 1976).

56. S. Matsuyama, R. Konoshita, and M. Segawa, Two layer permalloy circuits for 1.5 μm diameter bubble propagation, in AIP Conference Proceedings No. 24, American Institute of Physics, New York, 1975, p. 645.

57. I. S. Gergis, P. K. George, and T. Kobayashi, Gap tolerant bubble propagation circuit, IEEE Trans. Magn. 12(6), 651-653 (November 1976).

58. A. H. Bobeck, The development of bubble memory devices, in Proceedings of the IEEE Electro '77, IEEE, New York, 1977, Paper 12.1.

59. F. Yamanouchi, K. Yoshima, S. Fujiwara, and T. Furuoya, Bubble switch and circuit utilizing YY overlay, IEEE Trans. Magn. 8(3), 372-374 (September 1972).

60. R. Wolfe, J. C. North, W. A. Johnson, R. P. Spiwak, L. J. Varnerin, and R. F. Fisher, Ion implanted patterns for magnetic bubble propagation, in AIP Conference Proceedings No. 10, Part I, American Institute of Physics, New York, 1973, pp. 339-343.

61. Y. S. Lin, G. S. Almasi, and G. E. Keefe, Manipulation of 1 micron bubbles with coarse (>4 micron) overlay patterns, INTERMAG Conf. Dig. June 1977, Paper 11.6. Also IBM Research Report RC6513, May 1977.

62. O. Voegeli, B. A. Calhoun, L. L. Rosier, and J. C. Slonczewski, The use of bubble lattices for information storage, in AIP Conference Proceedings. No. 24, American Institute of Physics, New York, 1975, p. 617.

63. B. A. Calhoun, J. S. Eggenberger, L. L. Rosier, and L. F. Shew, Column-access of a bubble lattice column translation and lattice translation, IBM J. Res. Dev. 20(4), 368-375 (July 1976).

64. C. P. Ho and H. Chang, Field-access bubble lattice propagation devices, IEEE Trans. Magn. 13(2), 945-952 (March 1977).

65. H. Chang, Double layer bubble domain lattice system, U.S. Patent 3,996,571 (filed March 8, 1974; issued December 7, 1976).

66. Y. S. Lin, P. J. Grundy, and E. A. Giess, Bubble domains in magnetostatic-ally coupled garnet films, Appl. Phys. Lett. 23(8), 485-487 (October 1973).

67. J. C. Slonczewski and A. P. Malozemoff, Statics and dynamics of bubbles containing Bloch lines, in Proceedings of the AIP 18th Annual Conference on Magnetism and Magnetic Materials, American Institute of Physics, New York, 1972, pp. 458-477.

68. T. H. P. Chang, M. Hatzakis, A. D. Wilson, A. J. Speth, A. Kern, and H. Luhn, Scanning electron beam lithography for fabrication of magnetic bubble circuits, IBM J. Res. Dev. 20(4), 376-388 (July 1976).

69. T. H. P. Chang, M. Hatzakis, A. D. Wilson, and A. N. Broers, Electron-beam lithography draws a fine line, Electronics 50(10), 89-98 (May 12, 1977).

70. E. V. Weber and H. S. Yourke, Scanning electron-beam system turns out IC wafers fast, Electronics 50(23), 96-101 (November 10, 1977).

71. A. H. Bobeck, I. Danylchuk, F. C. Rossol, and W. Strauss, Evolution of bubble circuits processed by a single mask level, IEEE Trans. Magn. 9(3), 474-480 (September 1973).

72. M. H. Kryder, M. S. Cohen, N. J. Mazzeo, and J. V. Powers, A major-minor loop, single-level-masking bubble chip, INTERMAG Conf. Dig. June 1977, Paper 33.4.

73. E. Spiller and R. Feder, X-Ray Lithography, IBM Research Report RC6568, June 6, 1977.

74. B. J. Lin, Deep-UV conformable-contact photolithography for bubble circuits, IBM J. Res. Dev. 20(3), 213-221 (May 1976).

75. P. Chaudhari, J. J. Cuomo, and R. J. Gambino, Amorphous metallic films for bubble domain applications, IBM J. Res. Dev. 17, 66-68 (January 1973).

76. A. H. Eschenfelder, Bubble Materials—Amorphous vs Garnet, talk given at the International Conference on Magnetic Bubbles, Eindhoven, Netherlands, September 15, 1976.

77. A. A. Thiele, Theory of the static stability of cylindrical domains in uniaxial platelets, J. Appl. Phys. 41, 1139-1145 (March 1970).

78. P. K. George, A. J. Hughes, and J. L. Archer, Submicron bubble domain device design, IEEE Trans. Magn. 10(3), 821-824 (September 1974).

79. P. K. George and A. J. Hughes, Bubble domain field access device modeling, Part I: The magnetization Problem; Part II: Device modeling, IEEE Trans. Magn. 12(3), 137-159 (May 1976).

80. G. S. Almasi and Y. S. Lin, An analytical design theory for field-access bubble domain devices, IEEE Trans. Magn. 12(3), 160-201 (May 1976).

81. R. W. Keyes, Power and energy limitations in magnetic bubble devices, IEEE Proc. 59(10), 1528-1530 (1971).

82. R. W. Keyes, Microstructure Fabrication, IBM Research Report RC6366, January 20, 1977.

83. R. W. Keyes, Uncertainty and Information, IBM Research Report RC6215, September 20, 1976.

84. M. Takasu, H. Maegawa, S. Furuichi, M. Okada, and K. Yamagishi, A fast access memory design using 3 μm bubble 80 k chip, IEEE Trans. Magn. 12(6), 633-635 (November 1976).

85. R. F. Wickham, Projections of data processing memory usage, Proc. IEEE 6(8), 1096-1103 (1975).

86. B. E. Argyle, S. Maekawa, P. Dekker, and J. C. Slonczewski, Gradientless propulsion and state switching of bubble domains, in AIP Conference Proceedings No. 34, American Institute of Physics, New York, 1976, pp. 131-137.

87. Anonymous, Multilevel bit storage in CCD memory gives higher packaging density, Electronics 50(20), 65 (September 29, 1977).

88. H. Chang, Bubble domain memory chips, IEEE Trans. Magn. 8(3), 564-568 (September 1972).

89. H. Chang, Magnetic bubble technology—Present and future (Proceedings of the 7th Conference on Solid-State Devices (Tokyo), Jpn. J. Appl. Phys., Suppl. 15, 3-10 (1976).

90. E. F. Amelio, Charge-coupled devices for memory applications, in AFIPS Conference Proceedings, Vol. 44, 1975, pp. 515-522.

91. R. Melen and D. Buss, Charge-Coupled Devices—Technology and Applications, IEEE Press, New York, 1977.

92. J. M. Harker and H. Chang, Magnetic disks for bulk storage—Past and future, in Proceedings SJCC, 1972, pp. 945-955.

93. K. E. Haughton, An overview of disk storage systems, Proc. IEEE 63(8), 1148-1152 (1975).

94. U. O. Gagliardi, Effect of Electro-Mechanical Magnetic Memories on the Architecture of Data Management Systems, Stanford Research Institute Advanced Memory Concepts Workshop, March 23-26, 1976.

95. N. L. Rasmussen, Rotating Secondary Storage—A Limit to Growth, Stanford Research Institute Advanced Memory Concepts Workshop, March 23-26, 1976.

96. I. E. Sutherland, C. A. Mead, and T. E. Everhart, Basic Limitations in Microcircuit Fabrication Technology, ARPA Order No. 189-1, 7P10 Information Processing, Rand Corp., Santa Monica, California, November 1976.

97. EDN, Submicron IC Technology—From Lab Curiosity to Production, EDN, May 5, 1977, pp. 21-24. (Based on a report prepared by Integrated Circuit Engineering Corp., Scottsdale, Arizona.)

98. H. Chang, J. Fox, D. Lu, and L. L. Rosier, A self-contained magnetic bubble-domain memory chip, IEEE Trans. Magn. 8(2), 214-222 (June 1972).

99. H. Chang, G. E. Keefe, Y. S. Lin, and L. L. Rosier, Cylindrical magnetic domain decoder, U.S. Patent 3,689,902 (filed June 30, 1971; issued September 5, 1972).

100. H. Chang, Magnetic bubble domain processing apparatus and method, U.S. Patent 4,003,037 (January 11, 1977).

101. H. Chang, Re-writeable decoder, U.S. Patent 4,028,672 (issued June 7, 1977).

102. G. E. Keefe, Y. S. Lin, and Y. L. Yao, Bubble domain decoder with built-in memory, IBM Tech. Discl. Bull. 14(6), 1915-1916 (November 1971).

103. A. H. Bobeck and H. E. D. Scovil, Mass memory organization, U.S. Patent 3,703,712 (filed April 12, 1971; issued November 21, 1972).

104. K. Y. Ahn, J. V. Powers, and H. Chang, A Study of High-Resolution Full-Wafer Bubble Memory-Device Structure, IBM Research Report RC6340, 1977.

105. Y. S. Lee and H. Chang, Associative-search bubble devices for content-addressable memories, in CompCon '75 Fall Digest of Papers, IEEE, New York, 1975, Paper 8.2.

106. S. Y. Lee and H. Chang, Associative-Search Bubble Devices for Content-Addressable Memory and Array Logic, to be published.

107. A. M. Bobeck, H. E. D. Scovil, and W. Schockley, Magnetic logic arrangement, U.S. Patent 3,541,522 (filed August 2, 1967; issued November 17, 1970).

108. H. Murakimi, Cylindrical domain associative memory apparatus, U.S. Patent 3,760,390 (filed May 9, 1972; issued September 18, 1973).

109. H. Murakami, Multimatch processing systems with cylindrical magnetic domain elements, U.S. Patent 3,803,564 (filed February 27, 1973; issued April 9, 1974).

110. W. Kluge, Content addressable memories based on magnetic domain logic, Proc. IEEE 120, 1308-1314 (November 1973).

111. S. Y. Lee and H. Chang, An all-bubble text-editing system, IEEE Trans. Magn. 10(3), 746-749 (September 1974).

112. C. Tung, T. C. Chen, and H. Chang, Bubble ladder for information processing, IEEE Trans. Magn. 11(3), 1163-1165 (September 1975).

113. T. C. Chen and C. Tung, Storage management operations in linking uniform shift-register loops, IBM J. Res. Dev. 20(2), 123-131 (March 1976).

114. T. C. Chen, K. P. Eswaran, V. Y. Lum, and C. Tung, Simplified Odd-Even Sort Using Multiple Shift-Register Loops, IBM Research Report RJ1919, January 11, 1977.

115. H. Chang, Bubbles for Relational Data Base, to be published.

116. H. Chang and A. Nigam, Major-Minor Loop Chips Adapted for Associative Search in Relational Data Base, presented at 1978 INTERMAG Conference (Florence, May 9-12, 1978). To be published in IEEE Transactions on Magnetics.

117. D. K. Hsiao and S. E. Madnick, Database machine architecture in the context of information technology evolution, in Processing of Very Large Data Bases, IEEE, New York, 1977, pp. 63-84.

118. J. H. Wensley, The impact of electronic disks on system architecture, Computer 8(2), 44-48 (February 1975).

119. H. S. Stone, The organization of electronic cyclic memories, Computer 9(3), 45-50 (March 1976).

120. H. S. Stone, Parallel processing with the perfect shuffle, IEEE Trans. Comput. 20(2), 153-161 (1971).

121. M. C. Pease, An adaptation of the fast Fourier transform for parallel processing, J. Assoc. Comput. Mach. 15(2), 252-264 (April 1968).

122. R. C. Singleton, A method for computing the fast Fourier transform with auxiliary memory and limited high-speed storage, IEEE Trans. Audio Electroacoust. 15(2), 91-98 (June 1967).

123. T. Lang and H. S. Stone, A shuffle-exchange network with simplified control, IEEE Trans. Comput. 25(1), 55-65 (January 1976).

124. D. E. Knuth, The Art of Computer Programming, Vol. 3, Searching and Sorting, Addison-Wesley, Reading, Massachusetts, pp. 352-361.

125. J. M. Pavkovich, The Solution of Large Systems of Algebraic Equations, Stanford University Computer Science Department, RPT CS-2, December 6, 1963 (available from NTIS as AD 427753).

126. E. G. Coffman and A. C. McKellar, Organizing matrices and matrix operations for paged memory systems, Commun. ACM 12(3), 153-165 (1969).

127. C. B. Moler, Matrix computations with FORTRAN and paging, Commun. ACM 15(4), 268-270 (1972).

128. G. E. Forsythe and C. B. Moler, Computer Solution of Linear Algebraic Systems, Prentice-Hall, Englewood Cliffs, New Jersey, 1967.

129. D. M. Young, Iterative Solution of Large Linear Systems, Academic, New York, 1971.

130. H. S. Stone, The Solution of Large Multi-Dimensional Poisson Problems, NASA Tech. Memo TM X-62, 371, May 1974.

131. P. I. Bonyhard and F. B. Hagedorn, Request queueing for magnetic bubble memories, to be published by IEEE Trans. Magn. 1978.

132. M. Jino and J. W. S. Liu, Intelligent Magnetic Bubble Memories, to be presented at the 5th Annual Symposium on Computer Architecture sponsored by ACM and IEEE, Palo Alto, California, April 3-5, 1978.

133. T. C. Chen and H. Chang, Magnetic bubble memory and logic, Adv. Comput. 17, to be published in 1978.

134. J. E. Juliussen, Magnetic bubble systems approach practical use, Comput. Des. 15(10), 82 (1976).

135. F. B. Hagedorn, Long term testing of 68 kb bubble device chips, IEEE Trans. Magn. 12(6), 680-682 (November 1976).

136. R. A. Naden, W. R. Keenan, and D. M. Lee, Electrical characterization of a packaged 100 kb major/minor loop bubble device, IEEE Trans. Magn. 12(6), 685-687 (November 1976).

137. S. Y. Lee and H. Chang, An all-bubble text-editing system, IEEE Trans. Magn. 10(3), 746-749 (September 1974).

138. Y. S. Lin, G. S. Almasi, and G. E. Keefe, Contiguous-disk bubble domain devices, IEEE Trans. Magn. 13(6), 1744-1764 (November 1977).

139. T. Kobayashi, J. L. Archer, and M. T. Elliott, Bubble lattice file structure, U.S. Patent 4,059,828 (filed August 20, 1976; issued November 22, 1977).

140. H. Chang, Quadrature switches in read/write/clear decoder to allow chip interleaving, IBM Tech. Discl. Bull. 19(10), 4002-4006 (March 1977).

INDEX

A

Access
Adaptive delta modulation, 21
Airgap, 12
Amorphous films
   see Materials
Amplification, 9
Anisotropy, 1, 17
Annihilation, 7
Announcement system, 2, 3, 4, 13, 18,
   20-23
Architectures, 3, 20, 37, 76, 99-100
Associative search
   embodiment, 86-87
   latch operation, 88
   latch structure, 85
   versatility 82-83
   why bubbles, 83-84
   also see Data base
Asymmetrical chevrons
   see Bubble devices
Asymmetrical half disks
   see Bubble devices

B

Bias field, 2, 6, 17-19
Bibliography, 3
   also see References
Bubble basics, 3
Bubble-bubble interaction, 15
Bubble collapse, 6, 17
Bubble devices
   density improvement
     bubble lattice
      conductor access, 55
      field access, 55
     gap tolerant

(Bubble devices)
     asymmetrical chevrons, 12,
      53
     asymmetrical half disks, 10,
      12, 17, 53
     two-layer T-bar, 52
     Y-Y overlay, 54
    gapless
     contiguous disks, 54
   pick-axe, 10
   T-bar, 9, 10, 12
Bubble materials
   see Materials
Bubble size, 15, 16

C

Calculators, 13-15
CCD, 2, 3, 57, 69, 72-73
Characteristic length, 65-66
Characteristic energy, 65-66
Chevrons, 9, 11-12
   also see Bubble devices
Chinese character generator, 14
Chip
   bit capacity improvement,
     bubbles, 51
   bit capacity improvement, semi-
     conductors, 50
   capacity, 17
   capacity improvement, 71-72
     device and circuit cleverness
      bubbles, 52-58
      semiconductors, 51
     dimension reduction
      bubbles, 58-62
      semiconductors, 51
     die size increase, 51
   characteristics, 16

113

RETURN TO ➡ **CHEMISTRY LIBRARY**
100 Hildebrand Hall   642-3753

LOAN PERIOD 1	2	3
7 DAYS	1 MONTH	6
4	5	

ALL BOOKS MAY BE RECALLED AFTER 7 DAYS
Renewable by telephone

DUE AS STAMPED BELOW

JUN 0 1 1992		

UNIVERSITY OF CALIFORNIA, BERKELEY
BERKELEY, CA 94720   Ⓟs

FORM NO. DD5, 3m, 12/80